ST. ... AND
SL. MARY'S ...

W9-CJY-634

The
Hardhat's
Bedtime
Story
Book

054338

The Hardhat's Bedtime Story Book

AL CAPP

HARPER & ROW, PUBLISHERS

New York, Evanston, San Francisco, London

This book is dedicated to

CATHERINE

her enduring beauty and nobility

The Hardhat's Bedtime Story Book. Copyright © 1970, 1971 by New York News, Inc. World rights reserved. Printed in the United States of America. No part of this book may be used or reproduced in any manner whatsoever without written permission except in the case of brief quotations embodied in critical articles and reviews. For information address Harper & Row, Publishers, Inc., 49 East 33rd Street, New York, N.Y. 10016. Published simultaneously in Canada by Fitzhenry & Whiteside Limited, Toronto.

FIRST EDITION

LIBRARY OF CONGRESS CATALOG CARD NUMBER: 72-150591

CONTENTS

A Word from the Author   vii

The Story of Drooly   1
Harvey Overflow of The Famous Flushers School   5
Glimpses of the Finest Minds of Our Generation   6
Harvard, 1984; The President's Report   8
Advice to a Wed Father   11
Wrong Turn onto Sesame Street   12
Mothers Have Fertility Rights   14
How Not to Get an Honorary Degree   16
Father Knows Best   17
T. J. Trashbloom   21
Students Blow Up Buildings because Spiro Agnew
   Talks Mean about Them   22
The Day All Welfare Stopped   24
Meanwhile, Back at Académie . . .   25
How To Succeed without Really Marrying   28
Miss McFertile and Miss McFruitful   30
The Relevant Reverend   32
Tommy's Guests Tonight Are . . .   35
Dear Mummy   38
Anarchy, Anyone?   39
The Confession of Walter ("Criminal Scum") Birdseed   41
The Day after John Lindsay Was Inaugurated President   45
The Day after George McGovern Was Inaugurated President   47
The Sound of Cash and Music   49
Have You Seen Anything but Elliott Gould Movies Lately?   51
Charles Manson's Ideals Will Never Die   53
Mummy's Little Girl   55
The Short Reign of President William O. Douglas   57
If Paul Newman Leaves, What's Left?   59

A Girl's Folks Are Her Best Friends 60
We'd Have Free Speech in This Country if Spiro Agnew
    Wasn't Free to Make Speeches 62
You Can Learn a Lot From Educational TV 64
We Have the Whole World to Pick from
    so I Pick Shelley Winters 66
The Day Jane Porna's Life Changed 68
If Gloria Steinem Won't Listen to Me, Maybe
    She'll Listen to Harry Truman 71
A Stranger in a Disgustingly Familiar Land 72
Paul Newleft 74
Gossip about Stars of the Silver Screen 76
Will the Media Get the Message? 77
The Ramsey Clark Theory 79
Lo Finance 81
Don't Send a Boy on a Man's Job 84
Some of Your Best Friends May Be Practicing Conservatism 85
It's Legal to Run against Ted Kennedy in Mass.—
    It Just Isn't Good Taste 87
The Honest Eyes of Randolph Scott 91
A Day in the Life of Charles "Chuck" Puberty 94
Slobbidge Is My Name 96
The Plan of the Apes 98
My Honor, Your Mayor 100
When You Dine with a Gabor—
    You Pay Attention to a Gabor 102
The Day the Kids Wouldn't Swallow Silverspoon 105
Simple Pleasures of the Humble 107
Simple Pleasures of the Celebrated 108
How To Solve Crime in the Streets 110
The Psychos from Nebraska 111
Suffer Little Children to throw Molotov Cocktails 115
There's a Little Bulzcht in Every Culture Center 117

A WORD FROM THE AUTHOR

John Steinbeck wrote the preface to my last book (*The World of Li'l Abner*) and in it, he nominated me for the Nobel Prize. When they gave it to him instead, it broke his heart and I vowed that never again would I cause a great man pain. And so I have not asked quite a few great men to write this preface for me.

I hope you will buy the book, because once it's out, the market will be glutted with them. All the humorists who have been making fun of Middle America (and that includes all the humorists who know where their bread is buttered) will discover what a treasure trove the Left is of sanctimonious stumblebums and benign balmies, and will move into my turf.

Actually, I'll welcome them. It's been lonely here.

AL CAPP

Cambridge, Massachusetts

The primate wandered around the campus, living on snack-bar
bananas and dating Radcliffe girls.

THE STORY OF DROOLY

Harvbaked, the Ivy League university, inaugurated its new policy of dealing with student disrupters by appointing the leader of the latest student riot there to its all-powerful Board of Overseers.

One old grad complained that it was like appointing Richard Speck night watchman at a nurses' dormitory. The President retorted that, in his opinion, any Harvbaked student was as competent to run the university as he was. The old grad conceded that any man over 40 who considered any kid under 20 as smart as he, was probably right.

But the experiment had an unhappy ending when it was discovered that the student leader was actually an ape named Drooly.

According to an insider at the university, the story began last fall when Drooly was being shipped back to Pratt's Primate Paradise for a refund.

"He was one of six primates, including a ring-tailed monkey, two chimpanzees, and a pair of blue-nosed baboons, who were being used in an experiment to teach animals to talk," admitted Prof. John Kenneth Fagin of the behavioral sciences department.

"We had a year's grant of $22 million from the Department of Health, Education and Welfare," continued the professor. "We decided to limit our experiment to teaching each animal one word a year, for as many years as there are words in the English language, and apply for a new grant each year. Our future looked rosy.

"All the animals learned their word except Drooly. His word was 'fig,' but it always came out 'pig.' "

Ironically, that word saved Drooly from being sent back to the hell of Pratt's Paradise. He had been placed in a cage and was being loaded onto a truck when a group of Students for a Democratic Society passed and noticed him making obscene gestures, picking fleas from his pelt, and bellowing "pig!"

Recognizing him as a fellow SDSer, they liberated him by beat-

1

ing the truck driver and his helper into insensibility with the poles on which their peace posters were nailed.

For a week, Drooly wandered around the campus, living on snack-bar bananas, dating Radcliffe girls, and acquiring a reputation as a serious student by attending classes when everyone else was out demonstrating.

Then a riot erupted.

Thousands of young activists rampaged through the grounds, led by a young professor lobbing molotov cocktails into windows and belting anyone in his path with two yards of heavy tire chain. He was from the humanities department.

In the excitement, the professor stepped on an innocent spectator's hand. Unfortunately, it was Drooly's.

The ape bellowed the only word he knew, "PIG!"

The professor denied he was a cop. But Drooly would have none of that. "PIG!" he bellowed, "PIG! PIG!" He drowned out the professor's frantic objections until finally the students were convinced.

As they beat their former leader to a pulp, they shouted: "He was an FBI plant! He fooled us rank and file, but he didn't fool the groovy kid in the fur coat!"

They elected Drooly their new leader on the spot, and carried him on their shoulders to the president's office. They cuffed the venerable educator around a bit, ripped out his phone, tossed his files out the window, and then demanded student representation on the Board of Overseers, which was badly in need of youthful idealism. The President asked if the post of chairman would be satisfactory.

The student explained to Drooly that would give him the right to hire and fire faculty, accept or reject study courses, and oversee all college activities. It happened that at that moment, Drooly was dangling from the chandelier by his toes, trying to dislodge a wax banana from his gullet. The students interpreted the frantic shaking of his head as vigorous nods of assent, and for six months Drooly served as Chairman of Harvbaked's Board of Overseers.

Although he had a disconcerting habit of roaring "Pig!" when any of his fellow overseers tried to speak at a meeting, he won their respect by tossing student demostrators out the window when they tried to break up a meeting.

He was rapidly gaining fame as one of the nation's fairest and firmest college administrators when his true identity was revealed.

Professor Fagin had submitted a budget for more money when he noticed something strange, yet familiar, about the chairman.

What was strange was that he was the first chairman to indicate his displeasure with a budget by tearing it up with his toes. What was familiar was the way he kept picking fleas off his pelt throughout the meeting.

"It was Drooly, all right," said Fagin, "and when I realized that, I faced a moral problem. I agreed, of course, with all he stood for, but he *had* refused me more money. So I was forced to obey the dictates of my conscience, and reveal that he was nothing but an experimental ape on which a refund was due."

In closed session, the overseers quickly voted to award Drooly an honorary degree, relieve him of his duties as chairman, and discreetly ship him back to Pratt's Primate Paradise without making a fuss about the refund. But the story leaked to the press, and liberals of both parties rushed to Drooly's defense.

In an emotional interview on a TV talk show, Sen. George Mc-Grovel said that if we deprive one subhuman of his rights simply because he is verminous and violent, no student radical could be safe.

In a more moderate vein, Sen. Charles (Chuck) Puberty said that while he could not condone anyone hanging from a chandelier by his toes, he could not condemn anyone for stealing bananas if society did not provide a more dignified way of attaining them.

It was Drooly himself, however, who put a stop to the campaign to restore him to his high post at Harvbaked. His keeper translated his grunts to mean that he liked it better at Pratt's Primate Paradise. He met a nicer class of people.

One mail-order student managed to totally disrupt his school, 3,000 miles away, without leaving the house.

HARVEY OVERFLOW OF THE FAMOUS FLUSHERS SCHOOL

The most frustrated young people in America are students at correspondence schools. They are deprived of educational advantages all other students enjoy, since it is not only inconvenient to maim a dean by mail or close down a college by parcel post—it is almost impossible. But not quite.

One idealistic young mail-order college student recently managed to totally disrupt his school, nearly three thousand miles away, without leaving the house.

Harvey Overflow of Hastings, Nebraska, a student at the Famous Flushers School of Westport, Connecticut, had already completed his Fine Plumbing Arts course, winning high honors in Creative Tool-Forgetting, Extracting Diamond Rings from Sinks, and Making Improper Advances to Housewives.

It was when he was admitted to the Graduate School of Flushing, with its noticeably headier atmosphere, that he began to feel that something precious in him was going down the drain.

He'd read about the good other students were doing for society at non-mail-order schools: disrupting classes, mugging members of the faculty and showing their concern for education by making it impossible for anyone else to get one.

Harvey yearned to become involved.

He wrote an obscene letter to his dean, demanding that Famous Flushers take a stand on the inhuman flushing conditions in Indo–China.

The dean didn't reply, but the Accounting Department did, informing Harvey that he had put insufficient postage on his obscene letter, and they were adding the sum to his payment for his next lesson.

Deeply hurt, Harvey took his next lesson, a lead pipe he was supposed to run a plumber's snake through, and sent it back

5

attached to a spring mechanism that caused the pipe to hit the dean on the head when he opened the box.

The old gentleman's skull was fractured and, while he was undergoing brain surgery, the school expelled young Overflow.

The American Civil Liberties Union fought the case all the way up to the Supreme Court, where Justice William O. Bughouse, in one of his most far-reaching decisions, ordered Famous Flushers to readmit young Overflow on the grounds that the right of any intellectual to protest injustice, in any way he pleased, had been violated.

Famous Flushers refused on the grounds that young Overflow had sent insufficient postage to cover the costs of mailing the lead pipe, to say nothing of the brain surgery.

The government swiftly retaliated. The school's fourth-class mailing privileges were revoked, forcing it to close down, and leaving seventeen million students all over the world high and dry halfway through their flushing courses.

Although Harvey Overflow lost his chance to become famous as a Flusher, he has achieved an even greater fame. He is the only student who ever fractured the skull of a dean he had never met and closed down a college he had never seen.

GLIMPSES OF THE FINEST MINDS OF OUR GENERATION

"They are the finest minds of our generation!"

Are you tired of hearing that defense of young arsonists, muggers, dynamiters, foul-mouths, vandals, and punks who commit their crimes on campuses instead of in the streets, where they'd get a year in jail instead of a year at graduate school?

And do you wonder if they *are* the "finest minds of our generation"? And if they are, do you wonder if you're losing *your* mind?

Let me give you two looks into these "fine minds."

I live in Cambridge, Massachusetts, a stone's throw from Harvard.

After the bloody and obscene takeover of University Hall there, a town meeting was called at the Harvard Stadium to discuss it. Thousands attended—townspeople, moderate students, radical students and the surviving faculty.

It was telecast by the local educational TV station, which was strange, since they won't telecast bullfights.

When I tuned in, a student leader was speaking.

I could tell he was a student leader because he was wearing Leon Trotsky's old beard and the suit they found Che Guevara dead in.

That boy had an electrifying style. He was positive, compelling. He held the audience spellbound.

First he told the thousands in the stadium, and the hundreds of thousands watching television, how to run Harvard. Then he told them how to run the nation and the world.

My wife asked, "Don't we know that boy?"

"Of course, we do," I said. "Think of him without the beard. That's the student we hired last year to walk the dog. Every night he'd call us from Harvard Yard, panic stricken. He'd lost the dog. The dog had outsmarted him. The dog was home. So we fired him.

"Last year he couldn't run a dog. But this year . . ."

A few months ago, I arrived at the University of Michigan (where the SDS was founded) the day before I was to give a lecture. An SDS delegation called on me.

"You're lucky to be here this week," said the SDS spokesman. "Next week we're going to close the place down."

I asked him if they had any reason for doing it, or would they decide on one after they did it.

He said they had a reason.

They had discovered that the bookstores in Ann Arbor—there are five—were making a profit on the books they sold to students.

This so stunned and enraged the SDS that they demanded that the university open its own bookstore and sell books to students at cost. The finest minds of the SDS had discovered this would save each student $35 a year.

The university (which the finest minds of the SDS had not yet discovered is supported by the taxes of people who make a profit) refused. The SDS said they'd better do it, because more than half the student body wanted their own bookstore. The university refused again.

"So we've got to close the place down," said the spokesman.

I asked to be excused for a minute while I made a private call to a friend at the university's law school. With the information I needed, I rejoined the SDS delegation.

"You don't have to ask the university for your own bookstore," I said. "And you don't have to close the school, or burn it down. You say more than half the students want their own bookstore. There are 36,000 students. Exactly half would be 18,000. If each one chips in $5, you'll have a capital of $90,000 and you can open your own bookstore.

"Now that that's solved, do you have any other problems?"

The delegation rose and started walking out.

The spokesman said: "Your generation doesn't understand what we're after."

I said: "I think we're beginning to."

HARVARD, 1984;
THE PRESIDENT'S REPORT

CAMBRIDGE, MASS. May 23, 1984—The president of Harvard, Jerry ("Up against the wall, Mothers!") Rubin, announced to its Board of Overseers (formerly known as the Chicago 7) that his 10-year plan had been triumphantly concluded.

The announcement was preceded by a question from the dean of the law school, William ("Kill the Pigs!") Kunstler:

"Is somebody smoking a death certificate?"

8

"No, it's the medical school burning down," explained the dean of the Richard Speck School of Ethics "on orders from Chief Abbie ('Wanna blow your nose into *my* American flag, man?') Hoffman of the University Police (formerly known as the Crazies.)"

Chief Hoffman had uncovered evidence that the cancer cure perfected that very morning by the medical school was intended to be used in an effort to save the life of a dying young Marine. This of course violated the strict rule, adopted in the late sixties by Presidents Wiesner and Johnson of MIT, and by all universities by the early seventies, that no university facility could be used to aid any military effort. And so, according to the powers granted mobs by the Isla Vista Decision, the chief ordered the medical school burnt to the ground along with all its contents, including the cancer-cure formula. President Rubin told the Dean to compliment Chief Hoffman and order an extra ration of rape and rampage for his men.

He then read his Report for 1984:

"Ten years ago today, I was cleared of all charges, thanks to the gallant fight of the American Civil Liberties Union to make it illegal to punish anyone for any crime IF at the time, HE HELD ANY POLITICAL OPINION, on the grounds that this made him a political prisoner and it is wrong to suppress thought in a democratic society.

"My probation officer told me to get some sort of job that would keep me away from other maniacs, but I couldn't find one, and became president of Harvard.

"They felt I was ideal because of the William O. Douglas Decision. By 1974, as you recall, Justice Douglas was the only member of the Supreme Court. He *was* the Supreme Court, thanks to the precedent established by Sen. Birch Bayh.

"After defeating the Carswell nomination on the grounds that he was intellectually inferior, Senator Bayh carried his campaign to its logical conclusion.

"He demanded that the Senate disqualify, retroactively, *all* Justices who were intellectually inferior to, say, Justice Douglas. And it turned out they all were, since none of the others could prove that they, too, had had articles published by magazines devoted to hard-core pornography.

"Justice Douglas's first one-court one-man decision was the Wide Open Admissions Law. This made it illegally discriminatory for any college to refuse admittance to anyone because they were ignorant and didn't want to go to college, on the grounds that no one could *help* being born ignorant and not wanting to go to college.

"When the news of the decision reached a mob of 34,000 Weathermen who were smashing the windows of stores in Harvard Square, beating up the owners and clerks, and looting, as a protest against capitalist aggression and greed, they dropped their dynamite sticks and peace posters and rushed across the street to the admissions office.

"The Dean of Admissions stood up to the mob with the traditional courage of Ivy League Deans of Admissions. He refused to register anyone as a student unless they could measure up to Harvard's two remaining academic requirements: being able to inhale and exhale.

"As students, the 34,000 were entitled to choose their own faculty and president. As an economy measure, they chose to fire the faculty, and hired me, Jerry Rubin, as their president.

"My first official act was to find out how much bread Harvard had. It turned out to be nearly a billion.

"But it was invested in AT&T, IT&T, municipal bonds, and low-cost housing. Dangerous junk like that. So I reinvested it in a 10-year supply of pot, hash, horse, speed, and LSD.

"And for 10 years, we've all been stoned."

"Out of our skulls," agreed Dr. Timothy Leary, of the School of Transportation.

"There isn't a dime left," concluded the president, "but that's groovy because Harvard isn't worth putting another dime into. The buildings are rubble. The VD rate is the highest in the world, and Cambridge is a ghost town.

"My 10-year plan for Harvard accomplished all I promised it would, but I couldn't have done it alone. I owe so much to the little people. Little liberal professors who explained to the world that kids like me were frustrated idealists; little liberal residents of Cambridge who complained that the local police were over-reacting when they struck back after we brained them with rocks

10

and broken bottles, and most of all, to the liberal Boston papers, the 'talkmasters,' and the Boston educational TV station who called what we did 'confrontation' between the hope of the future and the barbarians. They called *us* the hope of the future.

"If people like us can depend on the continued help of people like that, we can do for the whole country what we've done for Harvard!"

ADVICE TO A WED FATHER

There are too many Ph.D.'s in this country, but not enough fender repairmen. Social scientists are a dime a dozen, but try to find somebody who knows something about a flush toilet.

If your kid shows promise of being a competent mechanic, don't turn him into a incompetent psychotherapist.

The great American tragedy is that so many of us think education can be acquired in ivy-covered buildings.

Any place that anyone young can learn something useful from someone with experience is an educational institution. It may be a garage or a machine shop. It can be outdoors on a construction gang.

Ours is the only society that considers a fine young mechanic so unnecessary that he's instantly bundled off to a boot camp but a student majoring in Bulgarian lyric literature is so vital to the preservation of the nation that he's excused from the risk of defending it.

WRONG TURN ONTO SESAME STREET

One day the White House called me. That doesn't mean the President. Lots of folks work there, and the help is allowed to make outside calls.

I was asked to serve on the National Reading Council, which was organized to combat illiteracy. The council met in Washington to hear a report from a panel consisting of Professor Rees of Princeton and Professors Lesser and Chall of Harvard on why so many people don't learn to read and how to get them to.

We were told that an increasing number of children are entering school with their willingness to learn how to read almost irreparably dulled, and with their physical ability to read already damaged, and the cause of it was TV.

Since TV is the cheapest babysitter and handiest pacifier, the harried mother is apt to plop her children in front of one from infancy on, where they remain transfixed and dulled through their most formative years. When they're old enough to be sent to school they are confronted with the vastly less entertaining printed page which their atrophied minds reject, and which their eyesight can't absorb, being impaired by years of looking from a distance at a comparatively immense illuminated screen.

And so since TV was the chief reason for illiteracy the panel had come up with a solution: more TV.

Not just *any* old TV, but one blessed program, one that one professor on the panel happened to be involved with, and that the other two, clearly revered him for: "Sesame Street," the educational network's multimillion-dollar triumph. What made it a triumph and worth the money they explained, is that a couple of million children are presumed to watch it, and are, thereby, exposed to its "commercials." These it was explained, seduce them into recognizing such letters as "x." No one explained why a kid *can't* learn what an "x" looks like from a commercial TV "Brand X" commercial as handily as from educational TV.

The panel agreed that since watching "Sesame Street" was the solution to illiteracy it should get another several million this year and the conference, including the producer of "Sesame Street" and several educational TV people, went along with that. But there's always one wise guy.

I pointed out that watching "Sesame Street" might, indeed, be one way to get kids away from TV and onto reading, but it seemed to me to be unnecessarily expensive and not wholly reliable.

It was unreliable because it spent only a fraction of its time teaching kids to recognize letters and, at that, no kid would ever see a letter in a book as big as the one on the TV screen. I also suggested that a kid could enjoy "Sesame Street" much as he once did the "Red Buttons Show" without paying the slightest attention to its commercials, as the sponsors of the "Red Buttons Show" can tell you.

I said that to pay millions in taxes (or tax deducted funds) for a TV show that theoretically attracted some of its audience of two million to reading might be impressive, but not to me. I said that "Li'l Abner" and a half-dozen other comic strips had audiences of 50-to-70 million a day—including Sunday—one-third of them kids . . . And even if only one-third of *that* one-third were attracted to reading by their eagerness to find out what the cartoon characters were doing, that was a far better score than a hundred "Sesame Streets," and it didn't cost a dime in taxes and never had. I pointed out that a kid could enjoy "Sesame Street" *without* learning how to read, but he couldn't enjoy comic strips *unless* he could read. And that a smaller investment in getting kids to read by supplying them with educational matter in such *reading* form—might make more sense.

At that, one after another member of the conference, mainly those with primary classroom teaching experience, rose to testify that, by gosh, now that I'd mentioned it, they recalled *they'd* learned to read themselves because they so passionately wanted to read the comics, and innumerable kids in their classes had, too.

The professors were astonished that they hadn't found out that comics were a powerful and proven way to lure kids to reading; and I said it might have been because they hadn't looked. Ivy

League educators, I said mournfully, turn their noses up at comics because they don't realize what most 7-year-olds do, that comics are simply arrangements of the oldest forms of communication, pictures and words, in their most compelling, beloved, and modern form. For educators to deem comics trivial as a literary form—because "Captain Marvel" is one is as absurd as to condemn books as a form because "The Love Machine" is one. Comics, I pointed out, can be a combination of the highest quality of art and text, and many of them are.

After the conference, most of the council, except those involved in "Sesame Street" and in getting more millions for it, thanked me. One said that he now realized that any mother who urged a kid to stop reading comics and watch "Sesame Street" was urging him to regress to illiteracy.

What'll you bet, though, that "Sesame Street" will get another $8—or $10—million next year, and that possibilities of the comic strip will continue to be ignored. They do the job—but they don't involve influential professors, you see—except as readers.

MOTHERS HAVE FERTILITY RIGHTS

Miss Ann Yewly Fruitful, mother of nine, was elected national chairman of MUMs (Militant Unwed Mothers) at their annual convention today.

"My administration," said Miss Fruitful, "will be an active one, and the action starts now. Some of you wondered why I chose billiard balls as luncheon favors. Well, put them in your purses, dearies, follow me, and you'll find out."

She led the 500 ladies to the nearest welfare office.

"Stand aside," she said to the cop at the door. "We are merely mothers, same as yours."

"Except for one technicality," murmured the cop.

"We're the last crowd in the world to worry about technicalities,"

14

she replied jovially. "Mothers love *all* children. And since all people, large or small, young or old, are always children to us mothers, we love *everybody*. So stand aside, pig."

He said something about being instructed not to admit anyone without an appointment, to say nothing of 500.

"We come in peace," said Miss Fruitful. "As you can see, we carry nothing but our purses. If you doubt that you can frisk us."

The cop said he didn't think that would be necessary.

"Oh, go ahead," giggled some of the more neglected MUMs. "We won't mind."

"Hasn't he *got* to frisk us?" asked some of the soft-core activists. "Isn't it his duty?"

"According to the regulations," replied the cop, "it's a matter of choice. And I choose not to. No offense intended."

The chairlady brained him with her purse, led the 500 ladies over him and into the office. They smashed the furniture, ripped out the phones, and tossed everything that wasn't nailed down out of the windows.

None of the employees dared lay a finger on them. One (new and poorly indoctrinated) phoned the Mayor to report that a mob of unwed mothers was wrecking the place, and asked if he didn't think they'd better send the police. The Mayor said he certainly would, if anyone tried to stop them.

When the place was a satisfactory shambles, the chairlady called a press conference.

"As an unwed mother of nine," she said, "I am entitled to lead a decent life. But what sort of meaningful, viable, relevant social activity can I expect when I'm too humiliated to make new friends because I must go on wearing minis when everyone else has switched to hot pants. Us MUMs demand an extra dress allowance whenever the styles change."

The MUMs all cheered.

"Then there's the matter of push-button TV sets. Why should us MUMs be deprived of them simply because we were too busy to get around to marrying the fathers of our children before we had them? There isn't an unwed mother in this room who hasn't worn herself out, getting out of bed 10, 15 times a day to change channels!"

"That's telling it like it is," cried the MUMs.

"But above all, we're concerned with the future of our children because goodness knows how many more we'll have in the future."

"Goodness has nothing to do with it," said a reporter, but one of the good aimers got him with a purse, and the speaker wasn't interrupted again.

"We demand a fully paid-up, four-year scholarship to the university of our choice dated 19 years ahead, one week after any of us starts going with a new fella.

"All these demands are nonnegotiable, and you'd better believe it. If you think this place is a mess, wait till the pictures come in from other welfare offices."

"Then this wasn't an impulsive gesture?" asked a reporter.

"It was about as impulsive as Pearl Harbor," chuckled the new generalissimo of the MUMs. "At the precise moment WE marched, hundreds of mobs of MUMs marched in every city in the country."

A kid reporter, on his first assignment from a rural weekly, piped up, "If you can march to the welfare office, why can't you march to work?"

Well, you wouldn't believe the avalanche of purses that zinged toward that kid, though Miss Fruitful begged the MUMs to have mercy, on the grounds that he was too new in the game to have learned MUMs motto: "No unwed mother should be asked to perform any other type of labor."

HOW NOT TO GET AN HONORARY DEGREE

Speaking at a banquet given by Boston University the other evening, I made one remark that transformed the attitude of my audience from warm disapproval to cold fury.

I said I was convinced that anyone who could walk to the welfare office could walk to work.

A Women's Liberation type rose and shrieked that only a

16

Neanderthal could be flip about a system so vile that it oppressed 20% of the population because they were poor, oppressed its women—over 50% of the population—because they were female, and oppressed 40% of the population because they were young.

During the ovation for her, I quickly added up some figures and then I said that either 110% of our population was being oppressed or the math course at Boston University was mighty weak.

I didn't get an ovation. I didn't even get dessert.

FATHER KNOWS BEST

In the last 10 years we have spent $8,684,000,000 on investigating slums and we've found 3 things about them: 1) that a slum is the least desirable part of any town (but also that the least desirable part of some towns would be the high-rent districts of other towns); 2) that nobody who can afford anything better lives in a slum, and 3) the smartest thing to do about a slum is work hard enough to get out of it.

The notion that we could totally eliminate slums has always been considered as looney as the notion that we could totally eliminate losers in a horse race or an election. Wherever there are winners, there must be losers, once seemed an unarguable truth.

But the looney idea that losers of any type could be totally eliminated, has now become law, thanks to a beloved clergyman, Fighting Father Looni. He first attracted national attention when, carrying a banner saying "I am Looni, so watch out!" he led 678 residents of a slum into a nice, middle-class, suburban neighborhood.

There, he and his followers invaded privately owned homes, moving in with the families already living in them, and refusing to budge, claiming they had "the right to share in the boundless wealth of America."

17

Father Looni then left the area to plan the seizure of other neighborhoods. When he returned two weeks later, he was shocked to see that the nice, middle-class, suburb was now a sleezy slum, with garbage reeking in the hallways, winos reeling in the streets, old tires and burnt-out cars replacing the well-kept lawns and flower gardens, and with crime having risen 598 percent.

Investigating, the deeply disturbed clergyman learned that the people who had once owned the homes had moved away, leaving the neighborhood to the new folks. In a flash, he realized he had the solution to the problem of urban life style that had eluded mankind since Sodom and Gommorah. He called a press conference.

"It's obvious," he said, karate-chopping a photographer who attempted to take a picture of his bad side, "that slums are caused by people. But *not* by the people who moved into them. It's the people who move *out* who are guilty because they had taken pride in them and kept their homes clean and in good repair, and their streets free of litter and trash. It's clear that when responsible people move *out* of a neighborhood it begins to go to pot.

"So the solution is to make it illegal for responsible people to move out," stated the humble man of peace, firing a round of buckshot at some responsible middle-class working people attempting to move out of their rapidly decomposing homes. "And also make it illegal for them to sell their homes to anyone *but* any irresponsible who can prove he can't afford to pay for it.

"The original homeowner will then feel compelled to remain on the premises to protect the house that represents his life's savings. He will keep it clean, in good repair, mow the lawn, and mop up after pot parties and stabbings.

"He and his family can move into the basement or the garage.

"In other words, my law will enable any stubborn unemployable or self-made undesirable to walk down any street in America, point to any house that appeals to him, and move right in, without the neighbors having to worry about it becoming an eyesore or lowering local property values.

"And that gentlemen, means FREEDOM! Complete, unhindered, groovy freedom! And isn't that what America is all ABOUT?"

The original home-owner will remain in the cellar, keep the house clean, and mop up after pot parties and stabbings.

T. J. Trashbloom, once a street cleaner, has been promoted to Engineer of Ecology.

T. J. TRASHBLOOM

T. J. Trashbloom of Manhattan was once a street cleaner. Since the great ecological explosion, he has been promoted to engineer of ecology. He once worked for the Department of Sanitation; he now works for the Environmental Protection Administration.

He gets the same pay, though, enjoys the same social status, and performs the same duties. Only he doesn't feel as good.

"If they go on with these Earth Days," he groaned to his wife one night, "I am not long for this earth. Everybody, from the mayor on down, suddenly discovers the city is filthy. So they get their pictures in the paper.

"I discovered the city was filthy the day I took this job 30 years ago, but nobody ever took my picture. The day they discovered the city was one big dump they called it Earth Day. The day I discovered it, I called it an ordinary working day.

"But there wasn't anything ordinary about Earth Day. You know how much litter we ordinarily pick up in the area of the Earth Day parade? About a ton.

"You know how much we picked up after the mayor's anti-litter demonstration on Earth Day? About 18 tons! And do you know how many extra hands the mayor provided to help us clean up? None."

"Maybe tomorrow will be better," comforted Mrs. Trashbloom. "All the anti-litter people will be off the streets, planning their next anti-litter campaign. So maybe it'll go back to that nice one ton."

"That would be great," sighed Trashbloom. "I don't want to deprive anyone, not even the mayor and his friends, of the right to protest the filthy state of this city by making it filthier, but I hope it takes them another six months to organize another Earth Day.

"Us street cleaners, I mean ecological engineers, can cope with a couple a year, but no more."

STUDENTS BLOW UP BUILDINGS BECAUSE SPIRO AGNEW TALKS MEAN ABOUT THEM

Mayor Lindsay of New York and Senator Ribicoff of Connecticut are usually in perfect agreement on such issues as that college students are forced to blow up buildings and people because Spiro Agnew is so mean to them, and that looters and arsonists are blameless; it's the police who are sent in to save the community from them who cause all the trouble.

And so it was dismaying when they disagreed a few days ago at a hearing of the Senate Finance Committee. The Mayor wanted $85 million more to solve his city's problems.

The Senator said that since New York's two major problems were that it was the filthiest city in the world and had the greatest number of idle, able-bodied welfare recipients, both problems might be solved by putting welfare folks to work cleaning up.

The Mayor snapped back that the Senator's suggestion to force idle, able-bodied Americans to do menial work was "rather extraordinary in view of modern thought" and would "bring us back to the Dark Ages."

The media carried his opinions to the entire nation before his plane carried him back to his office in New York.

He began dictating his daily denials that he would consent to be President to his secretary, but stopped when he noted that she wasn't taking anything down but her hair, which she usually wore in a prim bun, but which now flowed in a mad torrent of streaky gray to her hips.

"No more of this menial work for me," she announced gaily. "My true aspiration is to sing leads at the Met, but I was forced to be your secretary to pay the rent, and glad of the chance. But now I realize I was not only out of step with modern thought, but bringing us back to the Dark Ages. And so, until I'm offered the lead in *Aida,* where's the welfare office?"

22

The Mayor gave her directions and went out to his limousine. "Drive me to Gracie Mansion."

"No more of that Dark Ages stuff for me," replied his loyal chauffeur, stuffing his driver's gloves into the glove compartment and pulling on a pair of pearl-gray kids. "Is the welfare office still open?"

"In a truly modern city the welfare office is always open," said the Mayor proudly, and began to walk home.

He noted that the streets had an unusually festive air, that the crowds of strollers were unusually heavy, and that the stores were closed at an unusually early hour.

A cab driver pulled to the curb and yelled, "Hello, Mayor! Quittin' early?"

"Guess so," chuckled the Mayor, with his irrepressible wit.

"Me, too," cried the driver, taking his percentage out of the cash box and leaving the company's share and the ignition key in the cab as he abandoned it. "I heard what you said on the radio, and I'm wit' you. I am now a modrin thinker. Is there a welfare office near here?"

"There's a welfare office near everywhere," smiled the Mayor. "The nearest one is in that building on the corner where all the employment agencies used to be back in the Dark Ages.

As he passed the gigantic WOE (We Own Everything) Building, headquarters of the world's largest industrial complex, he noticed a stream of executives and secretaries pouring out, followed by elevator operators and maintenance men, all headed for the welfare office. Lastly came Otis P. Oatmeal, chairman of the board, an old buddy from Yale.

As Oatmeal was locking the front door, the Mayor said, "Closing for the day?"

"Closing for good," replied Oatmeal. "WOE has always prided itself on its modern thinking, so we're going out of business and onto welfare. We're the first major industry to do it, but I'm sure the others will follow. WOE has always led the way. So can you tell me the way to the welfare office?"

"I'll come *with* you, old buddy," cried the Mayor, tossing his briefcase into a manhole. "Being Mayor of a city with 120,000 able-bodied idle on welfare was a dream—but *if* the other 7 million won't work to support them, that nightmare I don't need."

THE DAY ALL WELFARE STOPPED

The day welfare stopped in New York City, and then, throughout the entire country, is now celebrated as reverently as Thanksgiving and Independence Day. It is a little-known fact, however, that the credit for the idea belongs to a forgotten group of San Franciscans.

Early in February, 1971, an account appeared in New York newspapers of the efforts of a dozen citizens of the Bay area to demonstrate imperfections in the welfare system. Although they were fully employed, they applied for welfare. No questions were asked, no identification was demanded. They were all promptly put on the welfare payroll.

One carried the idea a bit further and registered under four different names at the *same* welfare office on the *same* day.

That inspired a group of New Yorkers to carry the idea a bit further. They formed the Committee of One Thousand and Twenty-Five, a number which, when multiplied by 1,000, equals the number of welfare recipients in New York City, namely, one million twenty-five thousand.

Each one of the Committee of 1,025 registered at welfare offices all over New York City under 1,000 different names, all beginning with "A," and were sent a total of 1,025,000 welfare checks before any were sent to anyone else, since they are mailed in alphabetical order. This used up all the welfare money in New York that week, and every week thereafter, and stopped all welfare.

It was predicted that this would cause a ghastly rise in crime. Crime diminished instead, because a ghastly percentage of it had always been caused by welfare recipients robbing other welfare recipients.

It was predicted that hordes of hungry infants would roam the streets begging for crumbs of bread, because it had been highly publicized by the Welfare Department that over half of all welfare recipients were children. But that didn't happen either, due to a

24

less publicized fact: that one is considered a child by the Welfare Department in New York until the age of 21. And so the day welfare stopped was the day that hordes of husky youths applied for jobs the city had been unable to fill, such as cleaning up the city.

It was predicited that there would be demonstrations at City Hall by the city's unwed mothers, if welfare stopped. And, indeed, a mob of dreaded MUMs (Militant Unwed Mothers) did march on City Hall, but only to assure the Mayor that they hadn't lost one whit of the virility they had used in the old welfare days to tear City Hall apart, demanding more welfare money, but which they were now prepared to use earning their livings.

The day welfare stopped in New York City, thousands of bums, parasites and leeches all over the country stopped packing to come to New York City. And thousands of working New Yorkers, breaking under the welfare-tax load, stopped packing to move out.

The day welfare stopped in New York, the Mayor claimed there was no way his rotting, terror-stricken, half-abandoned city could survive without it, until a 14-year-old high school kid working part-time as a sweeper in the Department of Records discovered that once, in the dim past, there was no welfare in New York, and that not only had the city survived, but that it had grown into the greatest, strongest, most livable city in the world.

MEANWHILE, BACK AT ACADÉMIE . . .

I spoke at more than 100 campuses last year. The most frequently asked questions were:

STUDENT: What do you think of sex before marriage?

ME: It's beautiful before breakfast, it's lovely after lunch, and it's divine during dinner. That's not my opinion. It's a direct quote from Justice William O. Douglas.

STUDENT: What do you think of the maxi-skirt?

25

ME: It looks great on the fellas who design them.

STUDENT: What do you think of the mini-skirt?

ME: I think of them constantly. One morning this spring I arrived at an airport in the Southwest to deliver a Commencement address at a nearby university. The president met me and on the way to the campus we chatted. When we arrived we both fell silent. We simply stared, reverently, at those mini-skirts. Now, I am not a pious man, but I felt compelled to say "Heaven bless the man who invented the mini-skirt." The president said, "Why, Capp—*you* did! Nearly 40 years ago!" And do you know, I *did*! I put the first mini-skirt ever seen on Daisy Mae in 1934. They called me a pornographer then. Today, the world recognizes me as the benefactor of all the hip-and-thigh-loving mankind.

STUDENT: When was the last time you appeared on the Johnny Carson Show?

ME: The last time I appeared on the Johnny Carson Show I had the feeling it would be. My fellow guest was Mayor John Lindsay of New York City. He had just returned from a coast-to-coast tour in the interest of Nelson Rockefeller's presidential candidacy. And you all remember what a grand job he did for Nelson.

The Mayor said he'd come back distressed that there seemed to be an impression throughout the country that there were neighborhoods in New York City that a man couldn't walk through safely. And so he wanted to tell the studio audience and the millions out in television land that he, John Lindsay, had walked through every neighborhood in New York, and *he* had never been attacked.

Well, I said, I was mighty comforted to hear that. And that if I took my walks accompanied by legions of armed plainclothesmen, I would be just as courageous as John Lindsay.

But if I were the average New Yorker coming home after dark, I would be just as terrified as seven million others were that night of being mugged, mutilated, or murdered.

Well, I didn't hear much from Johnny after that, but I did hear from that studio audience. They stood up and cheered. If they hadn't been stopped they'd be cheering still. *They* didn't want to walk home alone after dark that night—

STUDENT: What do you think of our 11:30 P.M. curfew for freshman girls?

26

ME: Son, if you can't make out with a freshman girl before 11:30, there's no point in giving you an extra hour or two to make a darn fool of yourself.

STUDENT: What do you think of the birth control pill?

ME: It came too late. We really needed it when Jerry Rubin's mother said to Jerry Rubin's father, "I'm afraid we've been careless, dear."

STUDENT: What do you think of Dr. Spock?

ME: I loved that man when he was on diaper rash. But have you noticed, since he's left that area, how often he reminds us of it?

STUDENT: Have you any new solutions to the problem of student unrest?

ME: One. Let's stop calling it student unrest and call it by its proper name. When a gang of young punks registered as students at Harvard broke into University Hall, beat up two deans, and removed the contents of the safe, it was called student unrest. And they were given a year. At graduate school.

If a gang of young punks in Boston's ghetto, unregistered at any university, broke into an office, beat up the two men in it and robbed their safe, it would be called mugging and burglary, and they'd be given a year in jail.

I say let's stop calling student unrest "student unrest" and call it by its proper name: crime. We don't need any new solutions for that. We've got plenty of old ones on the books, if we have the guts to use them.

HOW TO SUCCEED
WITHOUT REALLY MARRYING

When the welfare mother of four living in a $75-a-day suite at the Waldorf complained that the maids didn't clean up until noon, the situation received national publicity and her plight was instantly rectified, but equally pitiable situations still exist behind the gaudy façades of other luxury hotels on Park Avenue.

Delicia DeVine stretched luxuriously among the silken sheets of her canopied bed in the Vanessa Redgrave Suite of the Regency Hotel and glanced at the porcelain and jade clock on her Louis XIV bedside table.

It was 12:15!

She must have fallen back to sleep after merely toying with her 10:30 breakfast tray, since the omelette cocotte and truffles were scarcely touched. She had, she now realized, slumbered on, undisturbed by the laughter of the children in the nursery.

She was about to call the manager and remind him, icily, that she had left instructions to have the suite cleaned up and fresh flowers arranged before her luncheon guests (the Action Committee of MUMs—Militant Unwed Mothers) arrived at one o'clock, when a panting maid entered with a mop and bucket.

"I'm sorry I'm late, mum," whined the wretched creature, "but your regular girl was too sick and . . ."

"Think nothing of it, Maybelle," smiled the queenly figure in the regal bed. "That *is* your name, isn't it?"

"It is, mum. Very kind of you to remember, mum," mumbled the menial.

"It's downright remarkable," chortled Delicia DeVine. "I haven't seen you since we were high school dropouts together, and you eloped with my boy friend Stanley!"

"Delicia Delinque!" exclaimed the careworn domestic. "Oh, how I've fretted all these years about stealing Stanley. But I won't fret any more, seeing how well off you are, married to Mr. DeVine."

"I never married any Mr. DeVine," chuckled her old chum.

"Never was any Mr. DeVine. That's just a name I like to go by. I never married anybody at all."

Just then one of the children ran out of the nursery, across the conservatory, and into the bedroom, sobbing.

"Mommy!! Lester rode over my four-speed, atomic-powered, miniature Apollo 14 rocket with his hydromatic, wide-track, radial-tired tricycle!"

"How many times," Delicia snapped, "must Mummy remind you she's not to be annoyed with your little quarrels. Just have the hotel manager call F. A. O. Schwarz's toy store, tell them to send another one over by messenger, and put it on the bill."

"Thank you, Mummy," gurgled the little tyke, rushing for the pink and gold nursery phone.

"And don't forget to instruct him to give the messenger a nice tip and to put *that* on the bill," cried Delicia after him.

"I won't, Mummy."

"I try to bring them up to be considerate to the working classes," she explained to Maybelle.

"I have one about that size," sighed Maybelle. "She wanted a rag doll for Christmas, but all we could manage was an orange and some nuts." Her voice broke. She dropped the mop and the bucket and fell to her knees, resting her head on the silken coverlet on her old schoolmate's feet, and wailed, "Oh, Delicia! We started off as equals, but ten years later—look at you and look at me! What did I do wrong?"

"You married the father of your children."

"But I loved him!"

"I loved the fathers of *all* my children," retorted Delicia, "but I didn't wreck my children's lives by *marrying* them. I kept a cool head. That's why *I'm* living at the Regency today, rent free, and *you're* living in a slum, worrying about the rent. Your future is grim. Mine is secure. The more children *you* have, the less there'll be to go around. But for every extra one *I* have, I'm paid extra."

"Some girls," moaned Maybelle, "have all the luck."

"Luck had nothing to do with it," replied Delicia tartly. "It was careful family planning. I planned my family so that nobody is legally obliged to support it, except Mayor Lindsay. And to him, bless him, there's nothing too good for a girl. Girls like I, I mean."

MISS McFERTILE AND MISS McFRUITFUL

"Something's missing," murmured Miss McFertile, glancing around the tastefully furnished apartment of her girl friend, Miss Mc-Fruitful. She had dropped by for their daily chat about the affairs of MUMs, but strictly the organizational affairs. "Something lovely . . ."

"It's Senator Sonny Silverspoon's picture," sighed Miss Mc-Fruitful. "He turned out to be the type a girl can't trust."

"They *all* turn out to be that type with us MUMs," giggled Miss McFertile.

"When he voted for Judge Blackmun, I trusted him. I said, 'What's good for Senator Silverspoon will be good for us MUMs when Barbara's case comes up.' "

"Barbara who?"

"Barbara from the Bronx. She is a Mum and is supported by welfare."

"And why shouldn't she be?" snorted Miss McFertile. "When a girl has given her country little citizens, shouldn't her country give *her* a little help?"

"I'll drink to that," cried Miss McFruitful, and did so. "Well, Barbara didn't cause any trouble until the day the Welfare Department sent a caseworker to visit her home. Barbara refused to let her in."

"I don't blame her!" exclaimed Miss McFertile. "I let one in a couple of months ago. The children cried all the time she was there. You see, not to upset her, I'd hidden the two color TV sets with the unwed mother next door, and the children had to watch the black-and-white set. But even after going to all that trouble, you should have seen the *look* that woman gave my *princess phone*!!! And when Harry From Out Of Town called up and asked if he could drop by for the weekend, I pretended it was the supermarket and I said, 'Thanks, but I HAD a delivery this morning!' Well, that eased the caseworker's mind, but it almost blew poor Harry's. He didn't catch on that I was talking about groceries. I'll never let another welfare worker into my home. Let them mail their checks and mind their own business is what I say."

"It doesn't matter anymore what you say, or what any of us MUMs say," fumed Miss McFruitful. "Barbara's case has been decided by the Supreme Court. And do you know what Senator Silverspoon's Justice Blackmun said? I'll read it to you: 'What this welfare recipient seems to want is the necessities of life *on her own terms*'!"

"Sounds as sensible to me," said Miss McFertile, "as anything Justice Douglas himself ever said."

"If he'd left it at that," replied Miss McFruitful bitterly, "he'd have been a shoo-in for MUMs Man-of-the-Year Award. But listen to the next sentence: 'One who dispenses private charity naturally has an interest in how his funds are utilized. The public, when it is the provider, rightfully expects the same.' "

"Our Senator voted for *him*?" gasped Miss McFertile.

"He did!" replied Miss McFruitful, "but this is one thing us MUMs won't take lying down."

"And the Supreme Court," retorted Miss McFertile, "can't force *us* to go on and on supplying the country with little citizens! They're not getting another one from me, and I advise you to do likewise."

"Too late," blushed Miss McFruitful. "Remember Harry From Out Of Town? Well, he was so upset at what you said when he called you that time, he dropped in to see me."

"And how is Harry?" asked Miss McFertile, without a trace of resentment.

"He's busy," said Miss McFruitful, "in the other room. Packing. He read that Supreme Court decision, too."

THE RELEVANT REVEREND

The Reverend Utter Chaos, the kindly Boston clergyman, yearned to become involved. So when he saw a bleeding policeman chasing 456 student protesters against violence, he granted the frightened youngsters sanctuary in his church.

"Just let me get my hands on one of them nonviolents!" pleaded the cop. "The one who brained me with the tire chain!"

"Braining folks with tire chains *does* border on the ill-bred," admitted the kindly clergyman, "but if I let you arrest the lad, there'll be a scar on his record."

A bleeding policeman was chasing 456 frightened youngsters.

"How about the scar on my skull?" the cop was saying as the kindly clergyman slammed the church door in his face.

The students gathered around their new-found benefactor and began to sing, "For he's a jolly good fellow . . ."

"Just trying to get involved is all," he demured modestly. But his face flushed with pleasure. He had never been particularly popular with the young before, and now he knew why. He had never been involved before.

"The church," he beamed, "must serve as a sanctuary for those who have faced the horrors of the outside world.

"The church must stop being merely a place to worship for those who built it and support it. The church must get involved in such vital causes as preventing the police from arresting people. By the way, why did that policeman want to arrest you?"

"Because we wanted to right the wrongs of society," cried all 456. "We wanted to end all wars, remove the rats from the ghetto, and eliminate poverty."

"Beautiful!" exclaimed the reverend. "And what fresh, youthful solutions did you bring to those problems that my generation had so dismally failed to solve?"

"Strictly nonviolent ones," replied the students. "We nonviolently dropped the draft board down the elevator shaft, we nonviolently set fire to the homes of all the owners of buildings in the low rent district, and we nonviolently lobbed a few fire bombs at squad cars containing potentially brutal policemen."

The Reverend Chaos then delivered a little sermon saying that while he questioned some of their methods, he was heart and soul with them in their efforts to remedy the rottenness of society.

"And speaking of rottenness," he chuckled, wagging a gentle finger at several students who were smashing open the poor box, "that money belongs to my church."

"Where do you get that *your* church jazz?" asked a student, ripping off his clerical collar and thwacking him across the face with it. "The church belongs to the people, remember?"

"And we're the people," gurgled another student, guzzling the last of the sacramental wine and hurling the bottle through a stained-glass window. "Don't forget that!"

"Is there a narcotics problem in the neighborhood?" asked the

"Where do you get that YOUR church jazz?" inquired the youngsters.

student who was counting the poor box money.

"Only in the junior high school," replied the clergyman, pleased at his concern, "and it's at its worst right now. It's recess time and the pushers come from all over . . ."

"Then hurry over there," said the student, giving a fistful of the poor box money, "and buy up everything those pushers have. We'll take anything, dig?"

"I dig!" cried the reverend, his face glowing with the joy of true involvement. "You wish to save those children from taking drugs!"

TOMMY'S GUESTS TONIGHT ARE . . .

Senator George McGrovel, whose groveling at the feet of the miniscule minority of the untoilet-trained on our campuses has won him the reputation as spokesman for all youth, was interviewed on the late-night TV talk show, starring the beloved Tommy Wholesome.

"The older generation," said McGrovel, "has failed abysmally!"

"Then *who* will lead America?" asked Tommy, who is also pushing 50.

"*Us youth!*" cried McGrovel.

The studio audience of runaways, high school dropouts, purse-snatchers and teenage unwed mothers cheered.

"You're not putting us on," ad-libbed Tommy with the quick wit that has made him a legend.

At this his producer held up the "CONVULSIVE LAUGHTER FOLLOWED BY PROLONGED OVATION" sign, and after the tumult subsided, McGrovel said, "The older generation *must* step aside, and let *youth* lead the way!"

They were interrupted by 243 commercials followed by 675 spot announcements, leaving Tommy only time enough to thank Senator McGrovel and announce his next night's in-depth interview.

"Who will lead America? Us youth!" cried Senator McGrovel.

Outside, the Senator hailed a cab and gave the driver his hotel address. The cab blasted off at 180 miles an hour through traffic, past red lights, and then hurtled down a one-way street the wrong way.

"*Are you out of your skull?*" screamed McGrovel.

"Just youthful zest is all, man," grinned the driver, turning around and revealing a New Left face peering out of an Old Testament beard.

"I'm a Columbia student making a few bucks for bail for my buddies who got busted at that 'Get Stoned and Stone a Cop Love-In For Peace . . .' "

"*Let me out of here, you half-baked idiot,*" McGrovel was screaming when the vehicle went out of control and crashed into the window of a mid-town store, which the owner had locked, barred, and fled from at the hour when New York City streets become too dangerous for business, 2 P.M.

The youth extricated himself from the smoldering debris and ran.

Since McGrovel's ankle was fractured, his hip dislocated, and his skull stove in, he waited for the ambulance.

En route to the hospital, the young intern examined him. "You'll need some pretty tricky brain surgery," he said, "and I can't imagine where we'll get a specialist at this hour. But don't worry, I'll have a go at it."

"Not at *me* you won't, you blundering amateur!" replied McGrovel, kneeing him with his one functioning leg.

The Senator insisted that an experienced surgeon perform the operation and during his convalescence he kicked out the student nurses the shorthanded hospital offered him.

"That stuff about trusting the fate of the nation to youth is okay for TV talk shows" he remarked later, as his white-haired nurse was giving him some time-tested medicine and putting him through some traditional exercises, "but you don't catch me trusting them with *my own!*"

DEAR MUMMY

Dear Mummy:

Much as I detest hypocrisy, I detest not getting money from home more, and so I am mailing this, as you told me to, in a way that will not attract Daddy's attention: in a KILL THE PIGS TO CREATE A NONVIOLENT SOCIETY envelope, with the stamps pasted over our peace symbol (J. Edgar Hoover with an ice pick in his skull), and I marked it "Personal to Mummy."

All this sham wouldn't be necessary, Mummy, if only you and Daddy weren't so Cro-Magnon. Can't you understand why I couldn't *bear* to waste another minute of my life at college, taking a pre-med course, and why I had to drop out and begin serving humanity in a truly *meaningful* way by devoting all I possess, such as my intellect, your checks, and my 38–22–32 self to comfort and sustain William K. Fowlemouth in his crusade to free all the members of the KILL THE PIGS Society from jail, where they are being held on trumped-up charges of rape, murder and arson.

Not that they *didn't* commit them, Mummy, but, as William K. Fowlemouth says, that's *irrelevant*. What *is* relevant, Mummy, is that they were committed for reasons too *beautiful* for your rotten system to understand.

I read that Daddy has been promoted to first vice president of Mom's Apple Pie and Bread Company, which—of course, he is too Neanderthal to understand—is simply an extension of the military-industrial complex, because, as William K. Fowlemouth explained to me, GIs eat apple pie and bread and *that* enables them to prolong the war.

William K. Fowlemouth also explained to me that a promotion like that also means a pay raise in Daddy's rotten system, and so, until we destroy it, will you send me an extra $200?

I'll bet you think it's for clothes, Mummy. That was the *old* me. This is the new *nude* me. The first time William K. Fowlemouth invited me to his pad he explained the sham and hypocrisy of wearing clothes. He was nude at the time and, after he made me understand the openness and honesty of it, I got rid of all my sham and hypocrisy and that's the way it's been with us ever since, Mummy, no sham and hypocrisy.

I need the extra $200 because I had to pay an outrageous price for a dozen boxes of genuine Havana cigars to one of the student sugar-cane cutters who smuggled them in after he was Fidel's guest to learn about capitalistic crookedness and greed.

You needn't worry, though, Mummy. Cigars aren't exactly what I and William K. Fowlemouth smoke. They're for Normie P. Newcash, the ex-poverty program official, who is being held on trumped-up charges of stealing $250,000 in poverty funds. You'd love Normie, Mummy. He's a truly warm, wonderful human being. He gave up a career managing the affairs of some girls on his street to become a humble $32,000-a-year poverty program official because he wanted to share the deprivations of the poor he loved.

While sharing the deprivations of the poor, Normie became addicted to Cadillacs, duplex apartments and genuine Havana cigars, and now he can't smoke anything else.

Normie is sure, though, that William K. Fowlemouth will get him acquitted before he finishes the cigars I bought for him, and when he gets out he promises to pay me triple what they cost me, out of a little nest egg he managed to stash away somewhere, somehow. So basically what it is, Mummy, is an investment. Better make it $300

POWER TO THE PEOPLE!

ANARCHY, ANYONE?

Dear Mummy:

In your dear old fuzzy Cro-Magnon way, I'll bet you and Daddy thought it was coincidence that I happened to come home the weekend you were away. Actually, Mummy, it was a revolutionary tactic, which William K. Fowlemouth says he has used before profitably. (And, oh, Mummy, he isn't merely a selfless defender of the right of arsonists and dynamiters to "do their thing" without being repressed by your rotten system. Since I left Wellesley and joined the revolution, William K. Fowlemouth has been a Mummy and Daddy and whatnot to me; a warm, truly wonderful Mummy and Daddy as well as a warm, wonderful whatnot.)

William K. Fowlemouth says he can't estimate quite yet what the profit will be on your jewelry I took, but he says at least we won't have to lay out any of it on bail money for me. Stupid, middle-class parents of your and Daddy's type, he says, never prosecute their *own daughters* for housebreaking and burglary, and so you'll notice that the station wagon and several of Daddy's suits are gone, too. But, oh, Mummy, they're going for a beautiful cause. The revolution against your rotten system, I mean.

I contributed your jewelry to the defense of "Icepick" Pickering, our Minister of Culture. Luckily, William K. Fowlemouth *is* the defense, so I didn't have to convert it into cash by dealing with a fence, which he says is illegal. I gave it all directly to the defense, and he put it directly into his, or rather Daddy's pocket, since the suits I took were for him to wear to court. He needed the station wagon for court, too, to bring something he was sure would persuade the jury to acquit Icepick. Namely, 27 of Icepick's friends.

I guess Daddy is pretty embarrassed for having said that William K. Fowlemouth was a more dangerous punk than any of the punks he represents, now that he's read about the brilliant legal maneuver that William K. used to get Icepick acquitted of those trumped-up charges of killing that pig.

The evidence against him was purely circumstantial, such as Icepick's fingerprints being all over the handle of the ice pick that was embedded in the pig's skull, and the sworn testimony of eight witnesses, the doctors, and two nurses that the dying pig's last words were, "Why did Icepick have to pick *me*?"

William K. Fowlemouth didn't even bother to dignify that irrelevant gossip by denying it. He plunged directly into the heart of the case.

"Sitting in this courtroom," he said to the jury, "are 27 of the accused's closest friends. I want you members of the jury to study their faces."

40

The foreman broke out into a cold sweat; one young juror with a twitch broke out into a rash; and a little old lady juror broke down completely.

"Do you know what you see in those faces," asked William K. Fowlemouth, "*deep interest*! Those 27 muscular young men are deeply interested in this case. They are deeply interested in you. They are so deeply interested that they have gone to the trouble of finding out where you live and what streets your children must cross when they go to school. They are also deeply interested in your verdict. And if it comes out guilty do you think they'll lose their deep interest in you? And *that,* ladies and gentlemen of the jury, is what I want you to think about."

The jury didn't even leave the courtroom to think about it. They acquitted Icepick on the spot.

Oh, Mummy, dear, with lawyers like that, and juries like those, I don't know why your rotten system even bothers to fight our revolution.

Please send the local papers. I'm interested in our state's legal abortion law. If they pass it soon, I may be home for awhile.

POWER TO THE PEOPLE!

THE CONFESSION OF WALTER ("CRIMINAL SCUM") BIRDSEED

Dear Judge:

I'm Walter Birdseed. Remember me, your Honor? You sentenced me to 20 years to life and called me "criminal scum," but I'm not complaining. I was guilty and I deserved it. But I want you to understand why I *had* to hijack Mayor Lindsay's limosine.

I'm from Wilkes-Barre, Pennsylvania, your Honor, and I came to New York City for a business appointment, planning to return that night. Not that I don't love the way Mayor has changed New York City night-life, but since the Korean War, my eardrums have been sensitive to gunfire and the screams of the wounded.

I'd heard about conditions at Kennedy Airport so I left on a 2 A.M. plane due to land at Kennedy at 3:45 A.M., which was lucky, because we circled until 11:30 A.M.

That would have left me ample time to make my 3 P.M. appointment if I could have found a cab, but all the cab drivers were at City Hall protesting the stick-up killing of a fellow cab driver the night before. I understand poor Mayor Lindsay is pestered this way every morning.

After waiting for three hours I found a bus with an empty seat. Making up the exact fare took all my small bills and silver, and I was left off 12 blocks from my destination, but I still had an hour to make it.

An empty cab came along; I hopped in.

The driver said he wouldn't budge unless I could show him the exact fare and a 15 percent tip. He couldn't make change because all the taxi change boxes are now locked. He said it was Mayor Lindsay's idea as a way to stop robberies.

I decided to take another bus, but when I asked the driver to change my twenty, he shoved me out of the door with his foot and took off, but was courteous enough to explain why, yelling back that busses no longer carried change, as recommended by Mayor Lindsay to stop robberies.

Same thing happened in the subway, your Honor. By then it was after 2:30. I was desperate. I tried stores—offering to buy anything, at any price, to get that twenty changed. No chance! It seems that no store in midtown Manhattan now keeps more than ten dollars in the cash register at any one time. When they accumulate more, they rush it to the bank, in an amored car, to avoid being robbed, on the advice of Mayor Lindsay.

I tried a bank. They were polite, but they explained to me that it was their custom to no longer make change for out-of-towners who didn't have accounts with them, as well as New Yorkers who did.

I looked for an outside phone booth to let my associate know I'd be late. But I couldn't find one that wasn't ripped apart. The phones in the office buildings were all ripped apart, too, except for one in a building next to Radio City Music Hall, but the line in front of that was longer than the line at Radio City Music Hall. Then

I had an idea. I went over to the most prosperous looking man in the line and pleaded with him to cash my twenty so I could get downtown.

He asked me for identification. I showed him my credit cards, my business card, my driver's license. He agreed to change my twenty.

When I reached into my pocket to get it, he mugged me. When I recovered consciousness, I was touched, your Honor, to see that those supposedly "hard-hearted" New Yorkers had been decent enough to keep the line moving *around* me, instead of *over* me, and a cop was picking up my nearest teeth. When he asked me what happened I explained, and he said that it was out-of-towners like me who made life unbearable in New York. A New Yorker, he said, would know that the most prosperous looking folks around are muggers because of the long business hours they put in. Even when they are caught, they don't get any rest. They are immediately let out on low bail, he said, because Mayor Lindsay says the city's jails are too crowded.

At that moment I heard a chorus of childish voices singing outside. I saw a procession of poor children marching in front of a limousine, strewing rose petals.

The cop explained it was the Mayor's limousine.

I leapt in, shoved my hand into my coat pocket, pretending I had a gun, and ordered the Mayor to instruct his chauffeur to take me to my appointment.

His Honor didn't answer me, your Honor, and then I realized that it wasn't the Mayor at all, but a clothing-store dummy with its eyeballs removed, which accounted for the uncanny resemblance. The real Mayor was back at City Hall, lowering the flag in honor of the martyrs of Brandeis University (students who were spoken to rudely after they shot Boston policeman Walter Schroeder, father of nine, in the back).

Unfortunately, the 712 armed plainclothesmen in the unmarked cars who always accompany the Mayor when he's anywhere near the poor folks who love him were not clothing-store dummies.

When they found out I wasn't a draft-dodger trying to get to Toronto, but a Korean War vet trying to earn a living, they dragged me off to jail quoting the Mayor's remark that veterans

"I realized it wasn't the Mayor at all, but a clothing store
dummy, which accounted for the uncanny resemblance."

like me were "not the sort of men I have unending admiration for."

I'm not complaining, your Honor. Mayor Lindsay certainly deserves a chance to clean up this town, and since there hasn't been a single mugger, rapist, burglar or dope pusher locked in here in the past six months I've been here, he must have.

Yours Respectfully,

Walter ("criminal scum") Birdseed

THE DAY AFTER JOHN LINDSAY WAS INAUGURATED PRESIDENT

The day after John Lindsay was inaugurated president his Attorney General, Ramsey Clark, moved into John Mitchell's office.

"In these files," confided his predecessor, "are the records of big dope peddlers we've collected enough evidence on to indict."

"Move 'em down the street to the National Headquarters of the Chamber of Commerce," chuckled the Nation's Chief law enforcement officer. "Soon as I legalize marijuana, and whatever else the boys are peddling, they'll be recognized for the legitimate businessmen they've always been, in *my* opinion, and in the opinion of my new Assistant Attorney General, Abbie Hoffman. They'll be waiting to join the Chamber, and I predict that in no time, they'll be running it."

"They're running everything else," muttered Mr. Mitchell as he left the city, and shortly after, the country.

At that moment, the new Secretary of Defense, Joan Baez, had summoned the Army's Chief of Staff.

"I assume, General," she said, "you know my Peace Plan from my albums?"

"I'm afraid I'm not much of a one for music," apologized the grizzled old warrior.

"Don't worry about it," smiled his slim superior, soothingly. "Without guitar accompaniment, it boils down to five words: *We must eliminate the Army!*"

"Which one?" cried the General enthusiastically.

"The U.S. Army," the Secretary said, "beginning with you."

"But ma'm, there will STILL be armies in *enemy* countries."

"Why should we solve their problems?" giggled the guardian of the Nation's security. "Let *them* figure out what to do with them."

"I bet they will," the ex-Chief of Staff muttered as he hurried out.

At FBI headquarters, J. Edgar Hoover's job was being taken over by Dick Cavett, who had qualified for it by inviting Ramsey Clark to denounce Mr. Hoover 712 times on his talk show.

He called for the Bureau's secret files. The top one was labeled: LYNCHING BY TV.

"Gosh," he said, "this is right up my alley. I was in TV once myself."

"Although lynching by rope is no longer practiced in the South," the report began, "a new twist, so to speak, lynching by TV, is on the increase in the North.

"The procedure is the same. Members of despised minority groups such as Republicans are lured by seemingly decent members of the community (TV talk-show hosts) to seemingly safe spots (the stages of late-night TV talk shows), and then set upon by buddies of the talk-show hosts, frequently including Truman Capote and Gore Vidal. These atrocities occur nightly in the sight of millions. Thousands, especially from mid-America and the South, write into the authorities (the networks), demanding that the TV lynch mobs and their leaders be restrained, but they are as contemptuously ignored as the Grand Kleagles ignored protests from mid-America and the North when lynching was done by rope.

"An example is contained in the TV tape which accompanies this document."

"This I've gotta see," quipped FBI Chief Cavett, unable to restrain the wit that in his TV days had made him the idol of so many intellectuals he had given free time to plug their books on his show.

He summoned an aide and ordered him to run the tape. To his disappointment it turned out to be a rerun of one of his own shows, but his good nature overcame his irritation.

"I never knew there was a sense of humor at the FBI," he chuckled. "Efram Zimbalist always looked so serious."

THE DAY AFTER GEORGE McGOVERN WAS INAUGURATED PRESIDENT

Although they laughed when he launched his campaign for the Presidency in the Spring of '71, it is now conceded that President-Elect McGovern won the youth vote by two inexpensive devices: letting his sideburns grow below his ankles, and the even cheaper device of demanding that youth take over all our institutions, except his own, the U.S. Senate, where no one under 30 is admitted, except the page boys.

His first official acts were to restore his original backer, Prof. Arthur Schlesinger, Jr., to his original position (horizontal) and to fire J. Edgar Hoover as head of the FBI.

The President-Elect stated that, although there had not been a breath of scandal or hint of corruption in the FBI in the 46 years Mr. Hoover had run it, he had three documents in his possession proving that Mr. Hoover was unfit. These, he openly revealed, were three unsigned letters from certain parties who claimed to be former FBI agents, saying that Mr. Hoover had been nasty and mean to them. And one Congressman charged that since he couldn't find the slightest evidence that Mr. Hoover had tapped his phone, that proved how tricky he was about it.

"The day of the tough cop is over," he announced to the press. "If society hopes to win the trust of its arsonists, muggers and thieves, we must demonstrate to them that the law is not their foe, but their warm, compassionate friend. And their warmest, most compassionate friend is the man I have appointed as new head of

47

the FBI—Ramsey Clark! In his book *Crime in America,* he proved something I have always warmly, compassionately believed: that there *is* no crime in America! Just folks so frustrated, they're compelled to murder and mug to regain their dignity. And so I have replaced Mr. Hoover with a man who will not stop any American from regaining his dignity, in any way at all!"

At that moment, at the Bureau, Mr. Hoover's replacement was addressing his department heads.

"The day of the tough cop is over!" he began, showing Mr. Hoover out and slamming the door after him.

"Er—Chief," interjected Chief Inspector McHammer of the Bomb Squad. "I have some photographs to show you. It's urgent, sir . . ." He placed one on his desk.

"That's one of the nicest shots of Charles Manson I've ever seen," was the chief's warm, compassionate comment. "It brings out all his boyishness . . ."

"It isn't Charles Manson," replied McHammer, "it's the National Commander of IMBECILE, a campus underground organization whose full name is Intellectuals Mobilized Because of-some-damn-thing-or-another, and what he's bringing out of that store are five alarm clocks!"

"Nothing wrong with a kid getting up early, is there?" bristled his superior.

"Depends on what his getting up for," retorted the inspector. He placed a second photograph on the desk. "Same kid," he said. "Different store. And different purchases. Five dry-cell batteries."

"You can't beat kids," chuckled his chief. "No matter how big they get, girls still play with dolls, and boys still play with electric trains."

"This boy," growled McHammer, "*could* be playing with an electric chair." He pulled out another photograph and barked:

"Same boy. Different scene. He's climbed over the fence surrounding the new Federal building under construction next door and he's sneaking past the guard toward that shack marked 'EXPLOSIVES.' That photograph was taken ninety seconds ago."

"Very interesting, but what business is all this of the FBI?"

"The FBI could be getting the business any second now," replied the inspector, glancing nervously at his wristwatch. "May I have your permission, sir, to take that boy into custody?"

"Certainly *not!*" snapped the chief. "He hasn't done anything wrong—yet. But *you* have. You have intruded on his privacy. Same as the Army intruded on the privacy of folks by taking *their* pictures just before the Capitol was bombed. The day of the tough cop is over, Inspector. We're bringing *warmth* and *compassion* into law enforcement. My order is to *destroy those pictures!*"

The order was instantly carried out, but not by the inspector. There was a tremendous explosion next door, and half the FBI building crumpled with it.

Although buried under the debris, the new chief managed to grab the ankle of a running young man who looked like Charles Manson.

"I didn't run this show long," he gasped, "but while I did— did I run it with enough warmth . . . and compassion?"

"Just enough, pig," replied the young man, viciously kicking himself free and heading for the Washington headquarters of the Civil Liberties Union.

THE SOUND OF CASH AND MUSIC

"Agreed then," snapped the oldest and hairiest of the three young men at the conference table, "we'll hold a gigantic rock festival to express youth's contempt for the money-crazed Establishment."

"RIGHT ON!" shouted the other three.

"We'll begin," he continued, "by hitting up each one of our dads for $100,000."

The youngest looked worried.

"I know what my dad'll say. He won't give it to me unless I promise to study at college and get a haircut."

"*All* our dads'll say that, man," chuckled the oldest, "so I move we agree with them, but once we *get* the bread, we tie it up in a dummy corporation. Then we call a press conference to announce our rock festival to show youth's contempt for the money-crazed Establishment, and we prove we're sincere by blasting our own dads for trying to buy our love and respect with money. Makes a nice tie-in."

"RIGHT ON!" agreed the other three.

"We'll put it in a corporate account, and only one of us can write checks. That'll be me, because I'm the only one who's of age."

This time the "RIGHT ON" was a bit weaker.

"The next thing is to decide how much to charge the kids."

"How about letting 'em in *free*?" cried the 17-year-old.

"You don't understand youth," said the leader. "They won't respect our rock festival unless we charge them a token something."

"A token dollar?" suggested the young one, idealism shining in his eyes.

"A token $56 like at Woodstock," said the leader. His eyes were shining, too.

"How about the kids that crash free?" asked one of the others.

"I've got that figured out," grinned the leader. "There are 5,000 karate schools in the area. I move we hire the students from those schools as ticket collectors and pay them a bounty of one dollar a head for every head they bash in of every kid that tries to crash free."

"A dollar a head isn't much," objected the youngest.

"If they're really karate experts they have an opportunity to earn more," replied the leader. "If business is slow, we can use them as ticket salesmen. *That'll* guarantee a profit."

"RIGHT ON!" cried the other two.

The young idealist was silent, thoughtful. Then he brightened up.

"You mean, of course, to give our profits away. To some fine cause. To some charity. Or welfare agency."

"I've thought of those possibilities," replied the leader. "And I've thought of another one: like funneling the profits into dummy Swiss companies with numbered bank accounts. Then we won't have to pay taxes to our rotten, materialistic government."

"RIGHT ON!" shouted the other two.

50

"You mean, I'm sure," persisted the youngest, unquenchably hopeful, "that we could use that profit to finance the revolution, to buy dynamite and things to help change this into a nonviolent society?"

"Sure, sure. Revolution," yawned the leader. "Well, the meeting is adjourned."

When the others had gone, he dialed a number.

"Like you predicted, Rocky," he chuckled, "them dumb little creeps didn't even *mention* the *big* rock festival bread. So I didn't mention it to them. We'll take bids on the drug concessions from outside pushers.

"That means we gotta split on all the drug traffic, but if the fuzz pulls a raid, we'll be clean."

"RIGHT ON!" said Rocky, and hung up.

The leader removed his fright wig, his false beard, his fringed leather vest, his peace symbol, his love beads, his tie-dyed jeans, and his sandals.

He pomaded his hair, powdered his blue jowls, pulled on a $450 silk suit, a pair of $275 alligator shoes, and walked around the corner where he had secretly garaged his silver Cadillac.

"You meet a lower class dealin' with' the youth market," he mused, puffing on his $3 Havana cigar, "but you gotta go where the bread is."

HAVE YOU SEEN ANYTHING BUT ELLIOTT GOULD MOVIES LATELY?

Lo Kunning, minister of the Department of Convincing American Youth They Live in a Rotten, Repressive Society and Should Hurry Up and Destroy It (known as the Hoff-Min, Ru-Bin Department), passed a plain tin box over the table of an outdoor cafe in Geneva to a young humanities major and dynamiter from an eastern university.

"In that box is one million of your rotten, repressive American dollars."

"I don't need all that!" exclaimed the young man. "Forty dollars worth of dynamite can destroy a major American city. A thousand dollars would be enough for *all* of 'em. Why, it took only a dollar and a half's worth at the University of Wisconsin."

"Dynamite is *out*," replied his slant-eyed friend. "Movies are *in*. They accomplish the same destruction, but they don't create a backlash."

"Folks *were* pretty upset when we blew up that research center in Wisconsin," admitted the young man, with a rueful smile, "but that was only because they didn't understand the nonviolent motives behind it."

"Dynamite," continued the Panther of Peking, as he was known to generations of geisha girls, "leaves a certain resentment. Used tastelessly it might even create a will to resist among the people.

"We must soften up your country. The surest and safest way to do it is with movies. Now you are 19—a bit older than the average American producer of 'message' movies—so you must be a bit smarter. Your movie must give the *other* side of student arson and homicide."

"Come out *against* it?" gasped the student, unbelievingly.

"Your hero," continued the cracked old voice remorselessly, "must tell his fellow students that while burning a college is useful, *learning* something useful might be an equally good way of improving American life."

"Keep your money!" cried the young man scornfully, rising from the table.

Pulling him back, the octogenarian Oriental hissed, "All that, my hot-headed young friend, is to establish credibility. Then," he chuckled, "in the confrontation scene we show what cringing, lying, slimy hypocrites the administrators are compared to the idealism of the SDS!"

"At last!" cried the young man, "a touch of *Realism*!"

"When the students begin to tear the place apart, because they are so 'understandably frustrated,' to use Senator Kennedy's phrase . . ." the movie comes out with its social message, which is that a clean-cut student can't get a date. But the filthy, foul-mouthed, dope-taking hero has hundreds of chicks crawling into bed with him. Elliott Gould could play the hero."

At the last words, the young man looked thoughtful. Then he sighed, and pushed the tin box back across the table. "That movie," he said, "has already been produced, and it's doing a grand job for you. It's called *Getting Straight*. Save your million dollars."

"I will," said the old man, watching him run for the plane back to the U.S., "But," he mused, "at my age—what will I save it *for*?"

He pondered for a minute and then ran for the plane, too, clutching the tin box and shouting: "DEFECTING! DEFECTING!"

"What for?" protested the young American. "In a few years we'll destroy our rotten, repressive system!"

"A few years is all I'll last," smiled the ex-minister, "and I want to have a few laughs."

He settled into his luxurious first-class seat to New York and made arrangements with the blonde stewardess to show him the town when they landed.

CHARLES MANSON'S IDEALS WILL NEVER DIE

Dear Mummy:

Will you please send my allowance checks to the Charles Manson Memorial Commune, formerly known as the University Y.W.C.A.

A commune, Mummy, is like a home, only it's nicer. In a commune people love and share with each other even though they are not bound by the hypocritical chains of marriage, like in yours and Daddy's degenerate society.

The people in our commune are Sally, Susan, Ruthie, Joanie, Jeanie, Betsy, Bonnie, William K. Fowlemouth and me. We'll need a larger one next year because then there'll be Sally and her baby, Susan and her baby, Ruthie and her baby, Joanie, Jeanie, Betsy,

Bonnie and *their* babies, William K. Fowlemouth and so on.

Oh, Mummy, what happened yesterday will make Daddy wish he'd died before he said that William K. Fowlemouth was a fouler criminal than any of the criminals he defended. Yesterday, William K. risked the lives of his loved ones—Sally, Susan, Ruthie, Joanie, Jeanie, Betsy and Bonnie—to *prevent* crime.

I'd been out to the Welfare office to collect our commune's monthly $2375 check, which really is not enough to keep us going until we destroy yours and Daddy's greedy, inhuman society, and when I returned no one was home except William K. Fowlemouth watching cartoons on TV. All the girls were gone and so was William K.'s gun collection.

He said the girls (and his collection) were out preventing crime, and he was so worried about them, he could hardly concentrate on the TV cartoons.

Just then the door opened, and in came Sally and Susan and Ruthie and Joanie and Jeanie and Betsy and Bonnie. They were giggling and carrying the gun collection and three tin boxes full of small bills and silver. William K. said, "How come there are only *three* boxes out of *four* gas stations?"

The girls explained that some state troopers had stopped at one to gas up.

Then, Mummy, I'm afraid I asked a stupid question. "Did you send the girls out to do something criminal at those gas stations?" He looked *so* hurt.

"My dear," he said. "It was the owners of those gas stations who were doing something criminal."

"You mean they were cheating?" I asked.

"Worse," said William K., "they *weren't* cheating. They were paying their *taxes*! And do you realize what those taxes pay for? Such crimes as equipping the Army with defense material, pensions for the widows and orphans of policemen killed in the line of duty, and Spiro Agnew's salary!

"By taking these tin boxes away from them, we've helped to prevent those crimes.

"Even more, this money will now be devoted to changing our crooked thieving system into something clean and honest."

"But," I said, "you're putting it all into your pockets."

"Who else," asked William K. Fowlemouth, "can be trusted

with it?" He then called a travel agency and asked them to reserve two first class tickets to Las Vegas and a suite at a first class hotel. Then he called a stripper named LaBelle. Then he left. He's been gone two weeks now.

Sally, Susan, Ruthie, Joanie, Jeanie, Betsy, Bonnie, and I all miss him terribly, Mummy, but those three tin boxes can't last forever, not at Las Vegas.

POWER TO THE PEOPLE!

MUMMY'S LITTLE GIRL

Dear Mummy:

No doubt dear old Neanderthal you and Cro-Magnon Daddy have read about that "atrocity" bombing of the Old Folks Home, and how a girl resembling me, accompanied by a blue-nosed baboon, were seen lurking around just before the fatal blast.

Well, that's just another example of the vicious twisting of the truth of your degenerate capitalist press, Mummy. I wasn't with a blue-nosed baboon. That was William K. Fowlemouth. I wish the degenerate capitalist press would stop describing his nose as blue. If you can't trust them to tell the difference between red and blue, what *can* you trust them to tell?

But the worst thing they said, Mummy, was that it was an "atrocity." If there is anything William K. Fowlemouth and I are committed to, it's peace, and I know the old folks we blew up realize it now, wherever they are.

The truth is, Mummy, we didn't intend to blow up the Old Folks Home at all. Ours was a purely military objective: The Col. Ethan A. Allen Home for Disabled Veterans.

Now it may seem unnecessary to blow up a hospital full of disabled veterans, but, as William K. Fowlemouth explained in his Address to the Troops (a young student who had dropped in, and our fellow occupants of William K.'s Commune; Ruthie, Joanie, Sally, Susan, Polly and their babies) it was a precautionary measure.

"I don't claim that GIs who have lost a couple of limbs can ever be brutal to Communists again," explained William K., "but they're still dangerous. Our researches show that once the average vet is rehabilitated, and makes good he generally votes REPUBLICAN!!!"

We all gasped, Mummy, except for Ruthie, Joanie, Susan, and Sally. They were plain angry. They said William K. shouldn't use obscenities in the presence of his babies.

"We must take precautionary measures," cried William K. "Who'll volunteer to toss the bomb?"

"I will!" cried the student.

"What are your qualifications for blowing up a Home for Disabled Vets?" asked William K.

"I am a humanties major at the University of California," he replied. "The San Diego campus."

"You are expertly trained," smiled William K.

Well, Mummy, the reason the Old Folks Home got blown up instead was due to a laughable mistake.

The youth sauntered down the block, and, as he was passing the Old Folks Home, a white-haired gentleman was raising the flag.

It was an *American* flag, Mummy.

Now I don't think the old gentleman meant to be divisive or to polarize the youth, but even Neanderthal you and Cro-Magnon Daddy can understand a University of California humanities major's frustration at the sight of an unburnt, unspatupon American flag.

Before he could control himself, he hurled the bomb at it and ran.

An 87-year-old lady victim was able to give a description of him, though, before she expired, and the forces of repression are now hunting for the brave young idealist.

Although he is sorry he lost his head, Mummy, he *is* proud that his school has won a place on the FBI's 10-Most-Wanted list. Up to now, it has looked like the dean's list at Brandeis University.

He wanted to hide out in our commune, but William K. said that, with Ruthie, Joanie, Sally, Susan, Polly, and their babies there, and all of them expecting again, there wasn't room for another man, especially a younger one.

POWER TO THE PEOPLE!

THE SHORT REIGN OF PRESIDENT WILLIAM O. DOUGLAS

(The following lecture on American History may be delivered by any professor in any American university fifty years from now.)

"Nineteen seventy-one was the year," the professor will say, "when youth came into power.

"A garland of bombs, secretly planted around Washington by a group of peace enthusiasts during a Moratorium, failed to go off (they were set for the wrong month), and were forgotten when a rock festival was announced for Earth Day.

"Long after the Moratorium and the rock festival left town the bombs exploded. The President, the Vice President, the entire Cabinet, and every member of the Supreme Court was wiped out, except Justice Douglas.

" 'I'm getting sick and tired,' said President Douglas in his inaugural address, 'of people yapping to me that although a half million Americans demonstrated for unconditional surrender in Washington, 199 million didn't.

" 'Those yappers miss the point.

" 'That half million were *concerned* citizens! That 199 million were *apathetic*! And you don't catch William O. Douglas running this country for a bunch of clods who go on apathetically working and voting instead of taking to the streets.

" 'And so my first act as Commander in Chief (and oh, baby, *is* it a first!), is to unconditionally surrender to all our enemies, everywhere. We'll show our goodwill by turning over to them our useless military-industrial establishment and all its products. They're bound to find *some* use for them. Also, we'll surrender the army, the air force, and the fleet.'

"This was immediately done.

"Clearly, in President Douglas, radical youth had found its voice, even if it was a bit quavery and constantly asking for the Geritol.

"While Peace reigned at last, undisturbed except for the quiet

57

beheading of all students and protesters in Communist-occupied areas and the occasional crack-up of our tanks in the eager hands of Communist learner-drivers, youth's first move at home proved to doubters that they were not impractical dreamers with no thought for the future. They began to build their new world.

"The first law youth passed was the Old Age Relief Law. Anyone over 30 was relieved of the necessity of voting.

"Also the right to.

"Youth's second move was to pass the Youth Relief Law. Anyone under 30 was relieved of the necessity of legally recording any more birthdays.

"In this way, youth was made a permanent condition, and youth was put permanently in control.

"It was when youth came up with its College Restructuring Plan that President Douglas revealed an unexpected streak of regressivism by disapproving of it. Youth showed its disenchantment by cuffing him about a bit, hiding his bifocals and publicly burning his truss. He threatened to call the authorities, but when they pointed out that *they* were the authorities, he signed.

"The College Restructuring Plan not only gave youth the right to hire and fire professors, but to *be* professors the instant they registered as freshmen.

"It also freed colleges from any necessity to do military research and all college youth (all youth now automatically entered college the instant they turned 18 whether or not they could read or write) were freed from the responsibility of military service.

"When President Douglas, fast losing popularity, grumbled that if youth wanted to enjoy those freedoms, they'd darn well better make *some* arrangements to safeguard them, youth replied that it was going to make the world realize that the only way to avoid war was to avoid doing anything warlike.

"And so, when their fellow youth, several million strong, from Red Asia, came wading in onto our Pacific Coast from their landing boats, our youth waded out to welcome them, offering them their hands in friendship.

"The Red youth grasped our hands, judoed us to our knees, and shot us through the head.

"Every one of us.

58

"Land sakes!" chuckled the little Oriental professor. "I don't know why I keep calling them *us*. Maybe it's because not long after the President did what youth wanted him to do there weren't any *more* of them—or anyone *else*—left. And the only ones who remember they ever existed are US."

IF PAUL NEWMAN LEAVES, WHAT'S LEFT?

Paul Newman and his wife, Joanne Woodward, may leave the United States and live in Britain, according to news reports. Newman said that although he had been approached by two states to run for senator, he is dissatisfied with America because, in his words, "there is a certain kind of insanity prevailing here."

"If two states have asked him to run for Senator," said his fellow star, rugged old John Wayright, "There *is* a certain kind of insanity prevailing here."

Another Paul Newman fan, Miss Ann Yewly Fruitful, unwed mother of 22 children and long prominent in community affairs, was equally saddened by the news.

"Paul Newman is speaking for all of us whom society has wronged," she said from the Vanessa Redgrave Pavilion of the maternity clinic built by federal funds for her and her sister members of MUMs (Militant Unwed Mothers), the organization of which she is president.

"We must do something to change his mind. Paul Newman threatening to leave the U.S.A. is comparable to Harold Stassen threatening to leave the Republican party.

"We can't allow this to happen. Although Paul Newman is over 40, a millionaire and a big wheel in many corporations, he has never lost his boyish zest for sneering at the ideas of anyone over the age of a college freshman and jeering at the profit motive. Those are qualities we *need* in our leaders. Besides, he *looks* cute."

Miss Fruitful was momentarily interrupted by the birth of her

23rd illegitimate child and then she continued, "We must restructure this country to satisfy Paul Newman!" She endorsed the infant's first welfare check and donated it to the MUMs Foundation for the Eradication of All Birth Control Methods, a noneducational institution.

"Our first move must be to repeal the discriminatory law that requires that anyone who runs for President of the United States must *live* in it.

"I sometimes think that law was passed just to be mean to Paul Newman.

"I say that if anyone as adorable as he is is willing to consider *being* President, the United States ought to be considerate enough to let him live in any country he *wants* to."

She then issued an order to take $39 million from the treasury of MUMs and use it to manufacture bumper stickers for the sports cars of every unwed mother in the country.

These will have full-color pictures of Paul Newman looking dissatisfied with the United States, and they will read: "Make Him Love Us or He will Leave Us."

It was only at Easy Rider Junior High, formerly Albert Schweitzer Junior High, that Paul Newman's threat created no panic.

"So what?" yawned an 11-year-old, lobbing a cherry bomb into a PTA meeting. "Have you seen his latest movie? I think he's leaving in the nick of time."

A GIRL'S FOLKS ARE HER BEST FRIENDS . . .

Jane Fonda has revealed a new side of herself to the public, which is the last thing the public expected of one who has revealed so many sides for so long.

Burning in Jane's ever-popular bosom is a passion to restore to our Indians the one thing, she says, they most yearn for: cultural centers in Oklahoma.

And so Jane led a band of 100 warriors on a raid of a U.S. Army fort, in Oklahoma, determined to rout the Army out and convert it into a cultural center.

Jane was defeated.

Now, if she had learned American history, from John Wayne westerns, as all red-blooded American kids should, instead of at Vassar, Jane would have realized that certain defeat awaits any band of warriors that attacks a U.S. fort.

Undaunted, Jane carried her struggle to the nation's supreme forum, the Dick Cavett show, where she revealed that she had detected a strong streak of militarism in the U.S. Army.

Jane's heart, as everyone who has seen her movies knows, is in the right place, but she should have a heart-to-heart talk with her Indians. She might discover that they're sick and tired of Oklahoma. Indians are like everyone else. They want to live in the *fun* places. New York—and Hollywood.

And there's a simpler way to get them there, than by demanding that the Army give its land back to its rightful owners. Armies are stubborn. Once they take a place, they figure *they're* the rightful owners.

Now there *is* a Fonda family town house in New York City, on land that rightfully belongs to the Manhattan tribe. And her brother, Peter, owns a ranch in California that, rightfully, belongs to the California tribe.

They are both much nicer, and handier, locations for cultural centers than any bleak old fort way off in Oklahoma.

And I'll bet that Jane's father and brother will be delighted to give them up to their rightful owners once she explains why they should. I'll bet they'll gently rebuke Jane for not having come to them in the first place, instead of going to strangers.

WE'D HAVE FREE SPEECH IN THIS COUNTRY IF SPIRO AGNEW WASN'T FREE TO MAKE SPEECHES

Three of the nation's most powerful decision-makers—a TV tycoon, a newspaper publisher, and the editor of a national news magazine—met in New York for lunch. They instantly plunged into their favorite subject: how Vice President Agnew has muzzled the media, stifled dissent, and deprived everyone of the freedom to say what they really think of him.

"If it weren't for that obese Aegean," growled the TV tycoon, "I wouldn't be facing a problem tonight with David Pinkley. He's willing to run a few minutes of the speech that bumbling buffoon is going to make this afternoon at Annapolis."

"Switched to Annapolis, did he?" sneered the publisher. "That hypocritical hack was invited to make that speech at Berkeley. And I understand those kids invested their entire month's allowance in stink bombs in anticipation of his visit."

"Just another proof of the administration's indifference to youthful hopes!!" snarled the editor.

"My problem," continued the TV tycoon, "is that Pinkley wants to run that flabby, neofascist's speech on a rear screen, with him live on camera, up front, sticking his tongue out at him, giving him Bronx cheers, and holding his nose."

"If you don't let him do that," cried his companions, "you'll be muzzling the media and stifling dissent!"

"By Rubin and Hoffman, you're right!" replied the TV tycoon. "I'm going to call him right now and tell him he's free to express any opinion he wishes about that halfwitted Hellene, as long as it's confined to nausea, mockery, derision, and contempt."

"I must run that speech, too," sighed the publisher, "and I don't know what headline to give it: 'AGNEW ASININE AGAIN' or 'VICE PRESIDENT VOMITS VENOM.' "

"Why not run the one that describes the speech most fairly?" asked the editor.

"The text hasn't arrived yet," replied the publisher, "so how can I tell? That wouldn't have made the slightest difference in the old days before that loud-mouthed lout robbed us of our journalistic integrity. I'd have used the most insulting one. But now that the reign of terror has begun, I'll have to wait until I read the text of his speech before I denounce it."

"You may think he's made it tough for you," groaned the news magazine magnate, "but he's made it even tougher for me. I have *two* cartoon covers drawn for this week's issue, and I can't decide which one to use. One is by Jules Trotsky. It shows Agnew sitting on a stool in a corner, wearing donkey's ears and a dunce cap."

"A probing satirist, that Jules," chuckled his mates. "He can say as much about American society with a few strokes of his pen as the entire Chicago 7 can with a few strokes of tar on an American flag."

"The other one is by Jules Lenin," he continued. "Agnew is in the same corner, sitting on the same stool, wearing the same dunce cap, but with cloven hooves, a forked tongue, and a pointed tail.

"But how can I tell, this far ahead, if Agnew will be more of a dolt this week than a devil?"

"The public wouldn't be so apathetic," muttered the publisher, "if it realized how muzzled the media is by Agnew, how he has robbed us of our journalistic fairness, and how terrified we are of uttering the slightest criticism of him."

"If you fellas aren't doing anything tonight," said the TV man, rising, "we're previewing a new comedy show. There's an imitator on it, David Freakout, who does an Agnew—*ha! ha!*—that will make that knuckle-headed Neanderthal wish he'd never been born."

"Can't make it," said the publisher. "Promised my daughter I'd drive down to the school for Fathers' Night. The girls have some great entertainment for us. They're going to burn Agnew and his whole family in effigy and dance around the fire."

"I'd love to," said the editor, "but I promised my kids I'd stay home tonight and play that new game with them—SPEAR SPIRO. It's the only one they'll let toy stores sell with *real* poisoned-tip darts."

YOU CAN LEARN A LOT FROM
EDUCATIONAL TV

On commercial TV you get actors merely pretending to be arsonists, muggers, and maniacs. On educational TV you get the real thing.

The other night, on a show produced in Cambridge, Massachusetts, on student unrest (which is what educational TV is trying to teach us to call arson and mugging when it's committed by students), one of the young performers resembled an Ivy League Charles Manson.

He wore the same style of biblical beard; he had the same look of one convinced he could walk on water.

As an undergraduate at Yale, he said, he had led sit-ins, takeovers, and rampages that had broken every law on the books. He was asked if Yale had punished him. His answer was cryptic. He said they'd sent him to Harvard Law School.

There, he said, he became one of the organizers and leaders of riots at Harvard Square, during which scores of small stores were repeatedly burned, wrecked, and looted, and their owners and clerks beaten, as a protest against capitalist violence, greed and aggression.

Did the educational TV producers stop that show and turn the self-confessed mugger, pyromaniac, and petty thief over to the Cambridge police?

They thanked him for his contribution. The specially invited Cambridge audience applauded him. Several members of the Harvard Law School faculty were on that show. They'd watched a criminal, aware of his constitutional rights, freely admit his crimes. They had a record of this confession on television tape.

Did the Harvard Law School expel him the next morning?

Did Yale apologize to Harvard for having given a college diploma to a compulsive criminal who had not yet completed toilet training?

Did it occur to anyone involved in this educational TV program that by this example they were educating the young the way Fagin did?

Has it occurred to any of the big businesses and the middle class whose contributions support educational TV that it is, obsessively and relentlessly, engaged in creating loathing for business and hatred for the middle class?

Not yet.

It may be because those who support educational TV don't watch it. It may be they feel it's worth the money to keep the creators of educational TV out of commercial TV, and vice-versa.

But every now and then one gets away.

Bill Woestendiek, a former editor of a national magazine, was hired as the producer of an educational TV news show, "Newsroom," coming out of Washington, D.C.

After a few weeks, he was fired.

Not because the show wasn't doing well. It was.

Not because he wasn't competent. He was.

Bill Woestendiek lost his job because his wife had taken a quasi-secretarial job with the wife of a Cabinet Secretary who was known not to be a liberal.

They called it "conflict of interest."

This was too much even for an editor of the *New York Times.*

He resigned from the show. He said that wasn't the way public television should be run. But anyone who works for the *New York Times,* or even reads it, should know that lots of public television *is* run that way. In Hanoi, in Peking, in Moscow.

Only there they don't call what Bill Woestendiek was fired for "conflict of interest." They call it "ideological deviation."

That's the difference between our public television and theirs, and pretty nearly the only difference.

The day after the Gallup Poll revealed that three out of every five Americans listed themselves, politically, as conservative, I called James Day of Educational Television to ask him if any one of their many production centers was run by a conservative.

He said he doubted there was one.

I asked him if there was a conservative in any decision-making position on any news or documentary show produced by educational television. He said he couldn't think of one.

Last year, when I was testifying before a senatorial committee, we got around to the subject of educational TV. I said that while Pete Seeger and Joan Baez, who sing chiefly of the indecencies of America, were given unlimited time on educational TV, rarely, if ever, had any time been given to those who sang of our decencies. And that I was convinced that we had some, and the educational TV audience should know about them.

Senator Charles "Chuck" Percy took umbrage at my suggestion that educational TV was slanted. Some of his best friends, he said, ran it, one of them being the commentator, Edward Morgan, and said Senator Percy, you couldn't find anyone more liberal than *he* is.

Senator John McClellan said, "That's exactly what Mr. Capp meant, Senator Percy."

June 7 and 14, 1970

WE HAVE THE WHOLE WORLD TO PICK FROM SO I PICK SHELLEY WINTERS

Do you wonder how guests are chosen for our popular nighttime TV talk shows? Let's look behind the scenes.

"I have a great lineup for you next week," cried the producer. "New faces! New ideas! Shelley Winters and Ramsey Clark!! David Susskind and David Frye! Jackie Vernon and Jackie Susann! Steve and Edie! The other Steve—the one they called Steverino when he had steady work—and his wife! Jerry Rubin and Abbie Hoffman! The lawyers for the Chicago 7 and the Panther 21! And, to give it a class finish, Truman Capote, Gore Vidal, and Margaret Mead!!! The Andrews sisters of culture!!!"

"A great lineup of new faces and new ideas," the star agreed. "But somehow it sounds familiar."

The producer lifted his eyes to the date at the top of the list and began to laugh.

"Small wonder," he chuckled. "That was *last* week's list. Here's the right one: David Susskind and David Frye, Abbie Hoffman and Jerry Rubin, Truman Capote and Gore Vidal. . . ."

"That certainly is as fresh a line-up of new faces and new ideas as any popular star could ask for," said the popular star, "but don't you still detect a resemblance to *last* week's list?"

The producer squinted at the date and burst into another peal of laughter.

"It was sharp of you to catch that," he chortled. "It's the guest list of the week *before* last."

"Also the week before *that*, if I recall correctly," the star said, "although recalling correctly isn't easy on our show. One week seems *so* much like another."

"I wonder if it does to our audience, too?" mused the producer, with a worried look. "I wonder if that's why we're being outrated by Randolph Scott reruns?"

He crumpled all the lists and tossed them into his wastebasket.

"Old Yale buddy!!" he cried, "Let's not fall into a rut! Let's get some *really* new faces—some *really* new ideas! We have the whole world to pick from. Everybody wants to get on TV talk shows, but no one ever seems to, except the same people who are always on!

"Let's lead off the week with a distinguished star of stage and screen who also has a light side. Someone, say, who can come up with the latest Spiro Agnew jokes. Someone, say, like Shelley Winters!"

"But doesn't that sound familiar?" asked the star.

"Naturally! Everyone has heard of her. And everyone has heard her Spiro Agnew jokes."

"But how about youth? The nation needs to hear from youth."

"Have I got some youths for *you*!" said the producer. "Jerry Rubin and Abbie Hoffman! The nation'll hear from them how Spiro Agnew is stifling free speech because, after they called him a fascist, a liar, a mass murderer, a clown, an ignoramus, and a pig, he called them coarse."

"Already," said the star, "it's as fresh and new a line-up of guests as there's ever been on any talk show."

"But," muttered the producer, his face clouding, "we need a fresh new face in the band. We must replace the trombonist."

67

"His playing sounds the same as ever to me."

"It's not his playing," rasped the producer. "It's his *laughing*. For two nights in a row, he *didn't* slap his knee while laughing convulsively at your opening monologue!"

"FIRE HIM!" cried the star. "There's no room in this organization for traitors!"

THE DAY JANE PORNA'S LIFE CHANGED

On what was to be the most important day of her life, Jane Porna was awakened by a call from her studio, asking her how she liked the new script they'd sent her, "The Girl Who Said Yes to Fellas Who Hadn't Even Asked Her."

"I'm not making any more of your rotten sex and nudie movies!" she shrieked. "It's humiliating to a girl who is pushing 33 and who has had two Caesareans and a gall bladder operation. I'm not putting a foot into a studio until you find me a good old-fashioned western! Cowboys shooting Indians! Redskins raping helpless pioneer women! Savages massacring paleface babies! The sort of family entertainment that has made the producers of CBS's 'Monday Night at the Movies' as rich as I'd like to be!!"

She slammed the phone down.

"Why are you crying, Mary Red Wing?" she asked her secretary.

"I d-don't rightly know," sobbed the 17-year-old.

"I can't stand a whiner," snarled the star. "I'm sending you back to Tulsa until you shape up."

Mary Red Wing packed and left. Jane waited three days for her studio to call again, and when it didn't, she called her public relations consultant.

"I've decided to take some time off between pictures," she announced, "and become involved."

"With whom?" he asked in a low confidential tone.

"With a meaningful cause!" replied Jane tartly. "I want to help some defenseless minority group no one has the guts to say a good word for."

"How about the Mitchells, Martha and John?"

"That much courage I haven't got," admitted Jane. "How about the Black Panthers?"

"The President of Yale has them under an exclusive. Anyone who tries for a piece of that action gets hit with a baccalaureate."

"Could I help the Chicago 7?"

"You must be kidding. With all those book royalties and lecture fees they could help you!"

"I guess everyone who needs help is used up," she sighed. "Nothing for me to do but go back to Hollywood and TRY TO GET INTO WESTERNS."

"Westerns," mused the PR man, "hmmn, there's an idea in there somewhere. Let's run it up the flagpole—What are westerns, basically? They're stories of how cowboys used to shoot Indians. Well, they get along fine now. There's no call for Indian-shooters now. So those cowboys must be out of work, and they must be old. That's it! You can help *old unemployed Indian-shooting cowboys!*"

Jane took the next plane to Oklahoma to find old Indian–shooting cowboys to help. The desk clerk at her hotel told her he knew some who needed about $40 million worth of help to drill some new wells on their old land, or they'd be forced to borrow on their old ranches, their old black Angus herds, and their old jets. Discouraged, she asked the clerk to send a maid up to help her repack. It turned out to be Mary Red Wing!

"You were trained to be a secretary," Jane gasped. "Why are you working as a maid?

"Because a maid who's willing to work can make more than any old secretary," chuckled Mary Red Wing. "Incompetent secretaries are a glut on the market, but a girl who can made up a bed can name her own price. My brother, Crawling Snake, was trained as a lawyer. Nearly starved to death until he became the men's room attendant here. Now he makes a fine living, almost totally tax free, and meets a better class of people.

"Our chief's son, Bonnie Prince Cochise, is an honor graduate of the Red Studies department of the state university. Made the dean's list in Fertility Dancing and Lamentations to the Great

"A maid who's willing to work can name her own price,"
chuckled Mary Red Wing.

Spirit, but a fat lot of good it did him. Now he runs the souvenir concession at the Greyhound Bus Depot. Cleared $18,000 last year."

"Educated though you all are, you're working at humble jobs," Jane cried, her eyes brimming with tears, "because you're Indians."

"Nope. Because we're smart," grinned Mary Red Wing.

Jane didn't hear that. Or anything else Mary Red Wing said. She insisted she follow her to the nearest U.S. Army post and demanded that the commanding officer instantly turn it over to Mary Red Wing and her folks as a cultural center. The C.O. turned them over to the state police instead, and they were all booked on charges of committing a public nuisance.

IF GLORIA STEINEM WON'T LISTEN TO ME, MAYBE SHE'LL LISTEN TO HARRY TRUMAN

Gloria Steinem, the Doris Day of Women's Liberation, came on the Dick Cavett show one night and complained about her problems. I came on a night or two later and solved them for her.

She had complained that when she walked through the Senate dining hall, the senators all stared at her.

I suggested that next time she might try wearing a mini that came down a bit lower than her navel.

She complained that girl reporters weren't given the same opportunities as men.

I recalled that Gloria was an obscure reporter until the Playboy Club hired her as a bunny, and she wrote an exposé of bunnyhood.

I said I'd bet that Norman Mailer wouldn't have been given the same opportunity when he was an obscure reporter, or even John Updike, although they both have great legs.

Instead of thanking me, Gloria fired off a telegram accusing me of not treating her like a lady.

With the gallantry that has made me a legend, I replied: "Dear Gloria: If you intend to go on sending scolding telegrams to everyone who criticizes you, you'll go broke. The day after I did, the *New York Times* did, and then Jimmy Cannon did, and then Bill Buckley did, and that's only the beginning.

"My advice, dear Gloria, is to remember what Harry Truman once said, 'If you can't stand the heat, get out of the kitchen.'"

A STRANGER IN A DISGUSTINGLY FAMILIAR LAND

Boris Bulzcht, the Russion film-maker, arrived in New York City today for his first visit to America.

As he stepped off the plane, he announced, through an interpreter, that he was instantly starting to write, direct, and produce a movie exposing this country as a rotten, racist society.

"But—" gasped a reporter, "you've only been here six minutes?"

"I know all there is to know about your rotten, racist society," he replied, "because I've consulted your leading intellectuals. I've talked to Jane Fonda by transatlantic phone. I've read all Paul Newman's public statements. I've listened to Joan Baez's records, and I spent nearly an hour discussing the United States with Eldridge Cleaver when my plane stopped in Algiers. I know as much about your degenerate, doomed society as anyone who has spent four years at Harvard."

"I still don't understand," persisted the reporter, "how you're going to expose our degenerate, doomed system when you don't even understand our language."

Through his interpreter, Bulzcht said, "Understanding the American language is unimportant. Artists understand a universal language: pain! The pain of the victims of your sick, hypocritical system."

He pointed through the window of the pressroom to a group outside: a cop speaking softly to a muscular young man, who was looking with a pained expression at an old lady on the ground.

"I understand the pain in that muscular young worker's eyes at the sight of his mother, whom that fascist pig has obviously beaten because she was wearing a peace symbol."

"I've just covered that story," said the reporter, examining his notes. "That muscular young man isn't a worker. He's a mugger on bail and on welfare. The old lady on the ground isn't his mother. Her son is in Vietnam. He tried to snatch her handbag. She fought back, so he belted her.

"That isn't a peace symbol she's wearing. It's a Jim Buckley button. As for the cop, he isn't going to beat up anybody, especially that muscular young man.

"He won't even dare speak rudely to him. See that indignant-looking chap in the homburg, stepping out of that Mercedes? He's from the Human Rights Commission, coming to protect the young man's human rights with bail-bond money and an invitation to a dinner party at the Leonard Bernsteins."

"So I got a few details wrong," chuckled Bulzcht. "Nobody's perfect! The important thing is I understand why your brutal, repressive system must be destroyed. And when the world sees my movie, they'll understand why, too. It will cost $235 million."

The reporter was impressed.

"*Your* country is going to spend $235 million on a movie about *my* country?"

"My country's got better things to do with its money" snorted Bulzcht. "Like build missile bases in Cuba. The money is coming from BACKSTAB, the international culture organization to promote brotherhood, 'B' and 'A' mean 'Basic' and 'Arts,' and the other letters mean I get $235 million."

"What nations contribute to BACKSTAB?"

"Just one. Yours. Who else can afford it? My movie will run for 27 hours."

"Isn't that an awful lot of Bulzcht?" asked the reporter.

"Movie audiences today," replied the great director, "can't get enough of it."

PAUL NEWLEFT

It isn't usual for a movie star to win the Nobel Peace Prize but, then, Paul Newleft isn't your usual movie star.

For one thing, this clear-eyed idol of millions has remained married for 23 years, 22⅘ of which he has been away making movies on foreign locations, spending a total of 12 weeks in 23 years at home with his wife and family to whom he is so deeply devoted.

Yet in spite of the years their marriage has endured; friends say they are as sweet and shy with each other as a couple of utter strangers. The Newlefts are beloved by liberals for having contributed billions of dollars worth of their prestige to liberal causes and by conservatives for having salted away a fortune of $112,000,000.

Yet they are homebodies.

They have a home in Beverly Hills, a home in New York City, a home in Connecticut, a chalet in Switzerland, a castle in Spain, and a chateau near Toronto. The latter is the favorite of their twin sons, Fidel and Che. For their 18th birthday, each boy was given a one-way bus ticket to Canada and predated allowance checks of $500 a week for the next 22 years. As they left they stated that they intended to stay in Canada forever to "get away from the repressiveness of American life and the draft."

They lived happily in Canada, issuing daily bulletins denouncing the lack of civil liberties in America and American militarism until the recent troubles, when all civil rights in Canada were suspended by liberal Prime Minister Trudeau.

The boys instantly took off in one of the family jets to avoid the "repressiveness of Canadian life and the possibility of being drafted into the Canadian army."

They have not landed anywhere yet, but they are trying to contact a country, any country which will guarantee to protect them in time of peace and not ask them to help out in time of war.

74

And we all, I'm sure, wish the boys good luck.

Paul Newleft's last movie, *Crass Butchery and the Gun-Down Kid,* played to a worldwide audience of 3,670,000 teenagers and netted the star a profit of $12,000,000.

It was a light-hearted story of two professional killers and gave its youthful audience a deeper understanding of the wholesome fun that killing folks can be. Following this, the star made a three-minute antiviolence short for the peace movement for no salary, just living and traveling expenses ($46,780).

It was shown to a total audience of 43 in a nudie drive-in movie outside of Medford, Massachusetts, between the sodomy feature and the incest cofeature and was withdrawn after one performance due to the hornblowing.

It was for this selfless sacrifice of his time and talent, this total commitment to principles he believes in, that Paul Newleft became the first Hollywood star to be awarded the Nobel Peace Prize.

On his departure for Stockholm to accept the award, and (so it shouldn't be a total loss) to also star in Ingmar Bergman's new film, *Sisters Are Swell for Seducing, but Mothers Are Marvelous for Matricide,* a morality play, which will take six and a half years to complete, Paul Newleft choked down his tears as he stated that his beloved wife could not accompany him, since, as comajority stockholder, she must take his place as chairman of the board of the Paul Newleft Small Arms Manufacturing Company, the Paul Newleft Big Arms Manufacturing Company, and the Paul Newleft Artificial Arms Manufacturing Company.

Upon his return, he has promised to devote all his time and talent to the Society to Combat Divisiveness and Polarization Caused by Spiro Agnew by narrating a 32-second film exposing the innate rottenness of the police.

Will this make Paul Newleft the first Nobel Prize–winning Hollywood star to become president of Yale?

GOSSIP ABOUT STARS
OF THE SILVER SCREEN

Joanne Woodward, who is married to Paul Newman, frequently gives American womanhood advice on how they, too, can achieve perfect and eternal bliss. In a magazine interview, she said, "A woman shouldn't sleep with a man who has differing political views."

Mrs. Mort Wineglass read that interview and tossed restlessly all night thinking about it. Finally she woke up Mort. It was 4 A.M. He asked what was wrong.

She said she couldn't tell him until he told her frankly what his views were on Ralph Nader. Mort said there were some things he agreed with Nader on and some things he didn't.

Mrs. Wineglass said there were some things *she* agreed with Nader on and some things she didn't. Then she kissed Mort, they went back to sleep, and lived happily every after.

The moral is: any girl's marriage can be as happy as Joanne Woodward's if she doesn't mind not being married to Mort Wineglass instead of Paul Newman.

Dustin Hoffman told a magazine that while he was filming *Midnight Cowboy* he suggested adding a scene. He said he wanted a black to come into a restaurant and sit next to him. Then he would get up and move and say, "I won't sit next to no black guy."

The director refused. A year later, Hoffman still thinks it should have been done. As realism.

Dustin Hoffman was wrong then. He is wrong now. White New Yorkers eat with black New Yorkers, work with them, marry them. So do white Californians and Kansans and Georgians, too.

The only Americans who persist in thinking other Americans are incurably bigoted are "concerned" actors like Dustin Hoffman.

It may be that only they are.

Jane Fonda's husband, Roger Vadim, has been paying a public relations firm to handle the publicity on Jane's campaign to help needy Indians, according to the papers.

You can't hire even the meekest PR firm to handle a big name like Jane Fonda for under $500 a week. If needy Indians were given that $500 a week, it might help them a lot more than spreading stories about how Jane Fonda is helping the Indians.

Now that Italian-Americans are picketing the FBI for giving them a bad name, I expect the Greek-Americans will be picketing Anthony Quinn for the same reason. Quinn was magnificent in *Zorba the Greek*. It was one of those roles that comes along once in a lifetime, and once is enough.

I saw Quinn do *Zorba* again the other night. This version was *A Dream of Kings,* and he called himself Matzookis in it, but it was old *Zorba,* all right. Same old philosophy, same old dance, same old scratching, same old nosepicking. In *The Secret of Santa Vittoria,* Quinn assumed an Italian name, but it doesn't fool us old *Zorba* experts. Same old accent as *Zorba,* same old underwear.

And so there is no reason for Italians to picket Anthony Quinn. He's a Greek problem.

WILL THE MEDIA GET THE MESSAGE?

When David Frost was driven from the studio stage while he was doing his TV show the other night by a mob of howling Yippies, I was saddened but not surprised.

I had warned Frost publicly on his show a year ago that he was setting himself up for it.

I know many of you remember that night because you still write to me about it and ask about it when I appear on lecture platforms.

A group of Yippies in the audience, you remember, tried to

interrupt me by howling quasi obscenities. Instead of groveling in the usual TV talk show guest fashion, I blasted them.

The Yippies, you recall, were stunned into silence.

But their host (he was mine, too, but that didn't seem to occur to him) spoke up for them. He said that it was unfair of me to react so—"brutally" was the way he put it—to a group of concerned idealists who represented American youth.

I said they were about as representative of American youth as the Mafia was of the College of Cardinals. Frost said sadly that in his opinion, my methods had "lost the audience." When the Yippies in the audience applauded that, he smiled gratefully. Then the mail from the TV audience poured in.

Of the first 1,000 letters, three agreed with Frost that my treatment of the Yippies had "lost" them. The other 997 said that it might help if talk show hosts like Frost got lost until they invited more guests who'd rub the Yippies' noses in their messes instead of trying to ingratiate themselves with them by rolling over and wallowing in them.

I sent the Frost people the mail, and told them to tell David that while it might seem smart showbiz to beg for the applause of the animals, those animals, if they were encouraged, would in the end devour the smart showbiz men who encouraged them.

I guess David Frost didn't get my message.

Now that they drove him from his own studio he seems at long last to have gotten theirs.

And maybe now others in the media will get the message.

The *New York Times* Sunday magazine, which more and more has come to resemble the campus underground press in its enthusiasms, not long ago carried an article defending the Berkeley Yippies who took over a million dollars' worth of university real estate which wasn't being used and announced they intended to use it as a "People's Park."

Does the *New York Times* think that, with this sort of encouragement, it will be long before New York Yippies take over Mr. Reston's car, while it is unused in the parking lot, and declare that a "People's Pontiac," or that they won't take over the unused cash in Mr. Sulzberger's wallet and declare that "People's Bread"?

A few weeks ago, the *New York Times* Sunday magazine ran a

cover story on Bob Hope, who has been entertaining troops in Vietnam, gently but unmistakably sneering at his "old-fashioned" politics.

They followed it with a cover story on Eldridge Cleaver, who has been entertaining the Learys in Algiers, full of unmistakable admiration for his "forward-looking" politics.

"There are advantages in political assassination," Cleaver told the adoring *Times* man, "it has great educational value. If Richard Nixon should be killed, I'd consider that an excellent thing. My ambition is the destruction of the American system."

You'd think our institutions—from the *New York Times* down to David Frost's interview show—which can exist only under our system, would be sane enough *not* to encourage their announced demolishers.

But they don't seem to get the message. Not until it's too late.

You feel like saying, "To hell with them—they deserve what they get."

But you can't.

Because when they get it, *we* get it too.

THE RAMSEY CLARK THEORY

Former Attorney General Ramsey Clark has announced his Peace Plan for the Seventies: he said, "If America cuts its nuclear weaponry in half the other fellows will have no choice but to follow."

This so impressed his admirers throughout the country that several of them decided to put Clark's theory in practice.

One large eastern city has a new, idealistic police chief, and a rising crime rate, but there I go—repeating myself. The chief called in his toughest crime fighter, Captain Ironjaw.

"I've decided," he said, "to use the Ramsey Clark Method to get rid of the Mob. Pull half your men *off* the streets immediately and send them home. When the Mob sees we've cut our weaponry in half they'll have no choice but to follow."

"You can't mean that, Chief!" ejaculated the captain.

"I do," he replied sternly, "and start now."

The captain reduced the police force to half its size. The chief waited for his first report about how the Mob had cut back, too.

"The report," said the captain the following night, "indicates that there were twice the number of muggings, burglaries, and homicides. But there are only half of the half-size force left. Quite a few of our boys were surrounded by the Mob, and knocked off."

The chief sighed.

"Look at it this way, sir," said the captain consolingly. "If the Ramsey Clark theory is that half the amount of police will stop crime *faster*—one quarter of the amount—which is just about what we've got left now—will stop it *faster*!"

"True!" exclaimed the chief. "We must never lose our faith in Ramsey Clark! I will go *on* reducing the amount of police. Starting now. With *myself*!" He packed his bags, dashed off a letter of resignation, and left town. Meanwhile, in New York City, Mohammed Ali switched to a new manager, who said he had a theory that would recapture the title from Joe Frazier.

"I adapted it," he told the ex-champ, "from Ramsey Clark's. The problem in the last fight was that you hit Joe with *both* hands. According to Ramsey Clark, that was wrong. Next time put one hand behind your back, and Frazier will have no choice."

When the night of the rematch in Madison Square Garden arrived, the manager called Ali from Palm Springs.

"No sense my leaving here," he said. "You know what to do. Call me when it's over."

Later that night, when Ali called, the manager said, "We must have a bad connection. I can hardly hear you."

"Maybe," replied Ali, "it's because I haven't any teeth left, and only one lip."

"What happened?"

"I did exactly what you told me. I put one hand behind my back, and, according to you and Ramsey Clark, he had no choice. Well, he had one. With a series of lightning rights and lefts, he knocked me out."

Meanwhile, in Hollywood, Elliott Gould's movies were losing money. So he fired his agent, and hired a new one, who claimed he had a sure-fire theory that would turn the tide.

"It's not my theory exactly," he frankly confessed to the star. "It's based on Ramsey Clark's theory that half as much of anything is twice as good. Translating that into artistic terms, in your next big love scene, wear half as much clothes as you usually do."

"That's impossible," replied Gould. "I never wear any."

"Then try the theory in *reverse*," cried the agent.

The star tried it. In his next big love scene, he wore pants and a T shirt.

The movie was a smash.

And that proves the Ramsey Clark theory that half as much of anything is twice as good, is bound to work, if it's applied sensibly.

It was worth millions to the public to see half as much of Elliott Gould.

LO FINANCE

It is a little-known fact that last year, the United States borrowed $100 million from Thailand, $20 million from Nationalist China, and $15 million from South Korea at the same time we were loaning them billions.

The reason this is not idiotic is that the principle on which our foreign aid is *based* is that our friends will always be as happy to help *us* as we are to help *them*. And they are, as long as they stay a few billions ahead.

One incident, however—an incident the State Department tried to hush up—threatened to end all foreign aid. We tried to borrow $48 from a tiny new country we've loaned billions to—Lo Kunning—but they turned us down as a bad credit risk.

We cabled, "What do you mean bad credit risk. We loaned you $580 million last year?"

They replied, "Anyone who'd loan us $580 million is a good credit risk?"

We cabled back that we'd pay 400 percent interest, monthly, twice the going Mafia rate. They replied that anyone who'd do that was a worse credit risk than they thought.

During these negotiations, the time came for our annual $580 million loan to Lo Kunning. It was promptly sent, in gold.

Our State Department, however, was terribly upset. If the story leaked, crusty old Congressman Wilbur Mildew, who thinks more of money than international brotherhood, might kick up a fuss and our entire foreign aid program might collapse, leaving billions that Americans earned for Americans to enjoy.

At this critical moment shy, poetic Senator Eugene McArtsy-Craftsy stepped into the picture. In his customary shy, poetic way, he called a secret press conference at Madison Square Garden to which only reporters from the *New York Times,* the *Village Voice,* the AP, the UP, Bob Dylan, Joan Baez, and Pete Seegar were invited, and announced that he would fly to Lo Kunning and seek a peaceful settlement of the $48 loan question with his old friend and fellow poet, Ho Chi Swine, the Lo Kunning Minister of Finance. He stated that, as usual, he wanted no fanfare; he was doing his duty as a plain, shy, poetic American, and he left, accompanied by photographers from no other publications than *Life, Look, Time, Newsweek,* and *Playboy,* and crews from no other networks than CBS, NBC, and ABC.

Stopping only at Toronto, Woodstock, London, Haight-Asbury, Paris, Tokyo, and the Berkeley campus to greet his youthful admirers and hold witty press conferences, the Senator's secret mission finally ended in Upaydforit, the capital of Lo Kunning.

Upaydforit was once six mud huts, a slave auction, and a public execution block; it is now a dazzling metropolis, a slave auction, and a public execution block, thanks to their embracing democracy and our gift of $22 billion.

The two old friends exchanged embraces, odes, madrigals, and Spiro Agnew jokes, and retired to the Temple of Chizla, god of Taking Candy Away from Kids.

The Senator explained that it wasn't the $48 any American was interested in (except for one American, Sol Kafka, a 67-year-old cab driver from Flushing. He needed exactly that amount to make up two days pay he lost when he was suspended by the N.Y. Hack Bureau for hesitating to pick up a 19-year-old junkie carrying a broken coke bottle, a meat cleaver, and a .44 pistol who wanted to be taken to an empty lot in the wilds of New Jersey at 3 A.M.).

What must be saved, explained Senator McArtsy-Craftsy, was the idealism behind foreign aid itself, since the United States was full of bigots and reactionaries who might stupidly say to hell with any country that won't loan us a few bucks after we've loaned them billions.

The Senator assured his old friend that he didn't expect Lo Kunning to go to any expense solving this purely American problem, but that he'd worked out a scheme, in iambic pentameter, that would save face for everybody.

All Lo Kunning had to do was add a $48 charge for "mail and handling"—the sort of thing the average dazed American pays without question—to the next shipment of $580 million from the United States, and then loan the $48 back to us.

This would make Lo Kunning not only look like good guys, but show a profit, since the 400 percent interest we'd pay on the $48.00, monthly, would amount to an extra $32 million a year in no time.

Ho Chi Swine said that, in the spirit of international brotherhood, he would accept the offer if we'd shut up about the $32 million interest and stash it away in his family's numbered Swiss bank account. He bade the Senator goodbye with an old Lo Kunning proverb:

"When the big goose who lays the golden eggs chickens out, the small vulture waits till he flies away before he gives him the bird."

DON'T SEND A BOY ON A MAN'S JOB

One young American who came to Washington on the recent end-the-war weekend didn't hitchhike or come by bus. He came by jet, and he came first class. He wasn't wearing a beard, love beads, or sandals. He wore a $600 silk suit, a snap-brim hat, and alligator shoes.

He didn't yell "Pig!" at the sight of a cop. He was particularly quiet when cops were around.

Our young man—let's call him Rocky—didn't join the mob at the Lincoln Monument. He checked into an expensive hotel. When he came to the line: Representing What Firm? he began to write an "M," crossed it out, and wrote "International Brotherhood, New York Branch."

"You interested in the peace movement?" asked the clerk, pleasantly.

" 'The less movement you leave in 'em, the more peaceful they are,' is the brotherhood's motto," replied Rocky.

Outside, the march had begun. Rocky didn't grab a "The Viet Cong Can't Be Wrong" poster. He grabbed a cab to the Pentagon. He was told that the Secretary of Defense was busy defending himself from 235 braless members of the Women's Liberation Front, who had inhaled in unison, pinning him against the wall of his office, and were beating him over the head with the collected works of Betty Friedan, and would he mind seeing their procurement officer instead.

Rocky said that would be okay because he had once been in procurement, himself.

"The Brotherhood has been follyin' your war wit' great interest," said Rocky. "At foist everybody was for it. Right?"

"Right," sighed the official.

"But they toined against it when it begun costin' too much? Right?"

"Right. It was when Senator Fulbright, Senator McCarthy, and

Senator Teddy discovered it was costing us $600,000 to kill each Communist that they noticed the war was against their ideals."

"I don't blame 'em," said Rocky. "You can do it cheaper. You gotta take it outa the hands of amateurs, which the U.S. Army basically is a bunch of, and let the pros handle it. Now, *my* foim . . . ain't no bunch of kids like the Army. We are professionals wit' branches all over. An' we woik neat. Wit' us, you can forget body counts. We don't leave 'em around. We will make you a contract at, say, five grand a hit."

The official, excitedly jotting some figures, said: "The U.S. taxpayer will save $555,000 for every hit."

"More 'n that," said Rocky. "How much do youse spend on equipment? Tanks, helicopters, bombers . . ."

"Billions!" shuddered the government man.

"All we need," said Rocky, "is a ample number of black Cadillacs, some silencers, and cement, ample cement. It is important likewise that the Cadillacs should have ample luggage space. But we don't expect you to go for no contract until you sees a sample of our woik. We will gladly give you a free one. Pick anybody."

The government man said no free samples were necessary.

"Suit yourself," said Rocky, leaving. "Except one thing I got to warn you. My foim expects prompt payment from the government. Any delay might be harmful to its health."

SOME OF YOUR BEST FRIENDS MAY BE SECRETLY PRACTICING CONSERVATISM

Once conservatism was a condition one confessed only to one's family doctor or priest but times have changed. A national survey recently revealed that three out of every five Americans now openly admit they are no longer latent but practicing conservatives.

In England the practice of conservatism is permitted between consenting adults, but we have been conditioned by Harriet Van

Horne and Dick Cavett to regard conservatism as loathsome, and those who are known to prefer it to natural pleasures are barred from the social studies departments of Ivy League universities, parties given by George Plimpton, the CBS documentaries division and all of educational TV.

And so conservatives, although cute as babies and often cuddled by liberals, are treated with revulsion and contempt as they mature. It is then that they develop unmistakably conservative traits such as paying taxes, even for government policies they disapprove of, obeying laws even those that inconvenience them, and not howling for revolution if they lose an election.

This has made conservatives cunning at concealing their condition and even "passing."

Sen. Eugene McCarthy, who is trying to regain the popularity he lost with youth when they discovered they had mistaken his menopausal capriciousness for high-minded statesmanship, "passes" by demanding that youth be given a chance to take over our institutions. While they cheer him, youth doesn't notice that the institution McCarthy so long belonged to, the U.S. Senate, still won't give any youth under 30 a chance, except as a messenger.

Jerry Rubin and Abbie Hoffman "pass" as the boistrous buffoons of liberalism by jeering at the U.S. Army for being violence-prone. The thought has not yet crossed any liberal mind that if the U.S. Army had not been violence-prone, Rubin and Hoffman would have been baked in Nazi ovens.

And Sen. George McGovern "passed" as a practical liberal when he announced not long ago that he was 1) against the population explosion, and 2) for giving a bonus of $65 a month to anyone who produced a new baby and all that brings up this question: If this country has been liberal enough to elect a haberdasher as President, then a rancher, will we be liberal enough to give an acrobat a chance?

When a man passes as a liberal, I want to know whose rights, whose property, and whose liberties, he intends to be liberal with. You can bet they're not his own.

IT'S LEGAL TO RUN AGAINST TED KENNEDY IN MASSACHUSETTS—IT JUST ISN'T IN GOOD TASTE

Challenging Ted Kennedy to a debate at a Catholic Young Adult convention banquet in Boston is comparable to challenging Golda Meir to a rassling match at a B'nai B'rith banquet in Tel Aviv, but I did it the other night, and every one of thousands of young Catholics there gave me a fair shake, including Ted Kennedy.

Kennedy and I had been asked to speak at that banquet months

Challenging Ted Kennedy to debate at a Catholic Young Adult banquet in Boston is comparable to challenging Golda Meier to rassle at a B'nai B'rith banquet in Tel Aviv.

before and, for months, it was simply a date on our calendars. However, a phone call in the week preceding it turned the date into a drama. It was from one not unknown for his interest in politics. He asked me if I would consider running against Ted Kennedy for the Senate.

I said it was unthinkable. He said he was glad I had an open mind and would I come to Washington and discuss it.

He and his friends began by expressing their admiration for Ted Kennedy. They agreed he was an honest champion of the radical liberalism he believed in, but they believed my conservatism was more radical, and more honest.

I said that I was always astonished when anyone called me a conservative. I said that I had once been a champion of liberalism, until it had gotten drunk with sanctimoniousness, and that if it ever sobered up, I'd champion it again. I said that today, there was on one side the flabby liberal, such as most of our TV talk show hosts; the fashionably liberal, such as Leonard Bernstein; the fanatically liberal, such as Justice William O. Douglas; and the frankly fascist liberal, such as Jerry Rubin and Abbie Hoffman. And on the other side there were the quietly sane.

And if the name of the sane was conservative, I'd accept that—but I wouldn't accept being called antiradical.

"A conservative," I said, "must be far more radical than a liberal. A liberal believes that anyone without work is entitled to welfare. A conservative believes that, too. But a conservative believes something more radical. He believes that anyone physically capable of demonstrating dissatisfaction with society with a firebomb or a broken bottle, can more vigorously demonstrate it with a pick and shovel—or a vacuum cleaner.

"A liberal believes that our young should be taught the faults and foolishnesses of America. A conservative believes that, too. But a conservative also believes that they should be taught a radical new subject, a subject so radical that those who try to teach it are howled down on campuses, and that is the greatness and goodness of America, the decency and generosity of Americans."

The fellows all beamed at me. "You go around Massachusetts talking like that and you'll be saying out loud what most people in Massachusetts are saying to themselves," said one. "You'll beat the pants off Ted Kennedy."

"But," I said, "I have so much going that I can't drop—a comic strip, a column, a radio commentary show—I couldn't guarantee to spend more than a day a week in Washington."

"Do that," said the fellows, "and you'll be the hardest working senator on Capitol Hill."

I said I'd go back to my studio and quietly think it over.

It wasn't very quiet at the studio, though. The AP, UPI, the networks, the news magazines, the local papers, and the London papers were on the phone demanding to know if I'd announce the next night.

The next night, at the Catholic youth banquet, there was one empty seat at the head table.

As the dessert was being served, there was tremendous excitement at the back of the ballroom. The camera crew began furiously setting up, reporters scurried, advance men cleared the way.

"He's here," the priest on my right whispered.

"I wonder if this late arrival was really necessary?" said the one on my left.

Ted Kennedy's presence created a genuine excitement in the ballroom that made the theatricalities of his advance man, advisers, and claque seem unnecessary and somehow degrading. I'd met him twice before.

The first time was at a party in Washington, years ago, celebrating Arthur Schlesinger's departure from the Johnson Administration. Art Buchwald and I were joint masters of ceremonies. Writing this, it occurs to me that there wasn't anyone present that night who, today, wouldn't celebrate my departure from the planet. (Where did I go wrong?)

I remember that I was surprised that Kennedy seemed so much warmer a personality and so much more instantly likeable than his brothers. I remember that we laughed a lot. A few months later, a huge, hatless youth stepped up to me in Boston's Logan Airport, thrust out his hand, and said, rather shyly, "We *have* met, Mr. Capp, at one of Arthur Schlesinger's parties. I'm Ted Kennedy."

We didn't meet again until that night at the Young Adult Congress banquet. The meeting would have been as unremarkable as the other two, if in the preceding week the press hadn't been full of rumors that I'd been urged to run against Kennedy by Massachusetts Republicans. I'd told the press I hadn't made up my mind, but that on the night of the banquet I'd make an announcement.

The kids in charge of the banquet said the excitement was running so high they'd decided to change the order of the program; the presentation of awards to come later, and the Kennedy-Capp statement to come immediately.

One of the Kennedy entourage asked if one more change could be made. On the program the Senator was scheduled to speak first.

I could understand the sense of changing that. After I made my announcement, it would give Kennedy a chance to respond.

"The rumor," I said, "that I am considering seeking public office has started other rumors. The one that hurts me most in liberal circles is that I am a flag-waver. There's a smear campaign going on that Al Capp would rather see our flag being waved than being burned. And it's true.

"It's true, too, that I have been urged to run against Senator Kennedy by those who feel that one household word should be opposed by another household word, and you can't deny that there isn't a household in Massachusetts that doesn't have a word for Ted Kennedy. Or for me."

I said that the prospect of a debate with Senator Kennedy was irresistible, and on any issue since there wasn't any issue I could rightly agree with him on. Even the issue he and I, as people, represented: the generation gap. I said I didn't agree with Senator Kennedy that those with the smooth skin of youth—like him—were idealists, and those with the wrinkled skin of age—like mine— were reactionaries. Some of the greatest idealists of our century were those with wrinkled skin: Gandhi, Schweitzer, Franklin D. Roosevelt. Some of the most Neanderthal reactionaries were those with smooth skin: George Lincoln Rockwell, the Hitler Youth. I said it seemed to me no more sane, or safe, to divide Americans by the conditions of their skin than by the color of their skin.

And I said I couldn't agree with Senator Kennedy on another issue: that the only way to preserve free speech for all was to make Spiro Agnew shut up. But, I said, irresistible as was the idea of running against Senator Kennedy, there were some thousand newspapers that expected me to keep "Li'l Abner" running, some 200 radio stations that expected me to keep my daily commentary show running, and an increasing number of papers that expected me to keep a column running. And that those commitments must be met.

And so, honored as I was by the confidence of those who felt I could win against Senator Kennedy, I could not run.

The Senator began with the ritual Spiro Agnew jokes, and then he picked up some cards and read:

"It really is a pleasure to appear on the same platform with Mr. Capp. There has been a good deal of talk lately that Mr. Capp is thinking of running for the U.S. Senate. If he wants to run, I welcome him to the contest. But I must admit I have some misgivings about his candidacy, as I can assure you that being a Senator leaves time for little else. So it becomes a matter of priorities. Do we, as a nation, want to sacrifice Al Capp to politics? Do we want to lose Li'l Abner, Daisy Mae, and Moonbeam McSwine? Is one vote in a body of 100 Senators enough to make us turn our backs on *all* the people of Dogpatch? I think not. I think Al Capp can do *more* for Massachusetts and for his country by leaving Li'l Abner alive, and I hope you join me in making sure he does."

Those were funny lines, written for the Senator by some funny men. He delivered them well. But nobody laughed. Possibly because they were lines written in response to an announcement of a candidacy. I had just announced I *wouldn't* be a candidate. But he'd used the lines anyhow.

I remembered reading somewhere that as kids, the Kennedys were taught never to waste anything.

THE HONEST EYES OF RANDOLPH SCOTT

Although His Honor the Mayor had said again and again, that nice as it was of groups of his more insecure employees to form clubs demanding that he run for President, he had no intention of doing so, he felt that the time had come to pick a campaign photograph, in case *his* party prevailed on the other party to nominate him.

He examined the pile on his desk.

"If Mummy had let me go into movies," he mused to his secretary, "I'll bet I'd have played Michael Caine roles. All my photographs have a shifty look in the eyes same as his has. Except," he held one up, "THIS one!! It is honest, open and clear-eyed."

"True," said the secretary. "It's Randolph Scott. One of the kids must have left it on the desk for you to ask him to autograph. Old–time stars are the big thing with kids now."

"Maybe us older folks can have some fun with 'em, too," chuckled His Honor. "Have our photographer superimpose his eyes on my face. And that'll be the official campaign photograph. What's next?"

"You've been invited to appear on the Dick Cavett show."

"Accept it."

"William Buckley will be the other guest."

"Cancel it. Find out when Shelley Winters or Jane Fonda is on. I come off as very intelligent with them."

"Who doesn't?" agreed the secretary. "You are scheduled to address the World Youth Assembly today at the United Nations, but . . ."

"Never mind the buts. I'll dictate the speech right now:

"Fellow Youth! Think of me as ONE of you—because I have been for over 50 years now. The world looks forward to us youth —to our idealism, to our fresh, vital, new insights, to our freedom from the petty prejudices and parochial passions of the past to deliver mankind from the turmoil, the ignorance, and stupidity that the older generation. . . ."

He paused and frowned. "You're not taking any of that down."

"I just heard on the radio that the World Youth Assembly broke up last night in a bloody shambles. They attacked each other like wild beasts."

"What else would you expect of a bunch of untoilet-trained little snots?" muttered the man who would one day be swept into the White House by the 18-year-old vote. "It's a crying shame, though, to waste all that great stuff about youth's idealism saving the world from the chaos that the stupidity of the older generation has gotten it into."

"Why not use it next week, when you address the Golden Age banquet? Those poor old souls have been told so often that *they're* to blame for the shambles the kids are making of everything, they'll take it meekly. By the way, John Wayne and Dean Martin may be backing your opponent."

"A fat lot anybody cares about the opinions of a couple of shallow-minded movie stars," snorted the future successor to Martin Van Buren and James K. Polk.

"Paul Newman is backing you."

"A deeply concerned citizen," he said reverently. "I will never forget his support of nonviolence. I will also never forget those yummy killings in *Butch Cassidy*. Saw it six times and had to wait in line every time. I'll bet it made him enough money to support him for the rest of his life. Paul Newman truly represents the deep sincerity of Hollywood liberalism. What's that gentle sobbing I hear from outside?"

"It's a group of mothers with a petition asking for protection for their children. The children are being mugged, molested, and their lunch-money snatched by the Sir Lancelots, a gang of sub-human teen-age punks, all on salary as guidance counselors at the Human Rights Commission. They say their husbands . . ."

"Those mothers are *married?*"

"I'm afraid they are."

"Tell them if they don't get off the premises in 10 minutes I'll have them run in for soliciting!"

"Is that the sound of furniture being smashed?"

"Yes! It's another group of mothers—Unwed mothers, asking for . . ."

"Never mind *what* they're asking for! Give 'em anything they want! If there's one group all true liberals respect, it's mothers! But only if they're unwed. I guess that does it for today, doesn't it?"

"Except for one thing. Your daily blast against Spiro Agnew."

"What did *he* do yesterday?"

"Absolutely nothing. It's going to be hard to blast him for that."

"Not for me," he chuckled.

"Release this statement to all the news services: 'While hundreds of thousands of Americans cannot afford cab fare to their welfare offices; while others must wait for their monthly replacements for the light fixtures and toilet seats they've ripped out of their public housing and sold; what does our Vice President do? Absolutely nothing! In this way, he is polarizing society, antagonizing youth, and prolonging the war!' "

A DAY IN THE LIFE OF CHARLES "CHUCK" PUBERTY

Sen. Charles "Chuck" Puberty never smoked, drank, chewed, cussed, or fooled around in his youth. He started as a loyal employee of a component of the military-industrial complex and rose to be a cost-cutting executive. He sold out to a conglomerate and, at the age of 30, having amassed a personal fortune of $30 million, he went into politics as an anti-Establishment liberal.

Although now pushing 50, his strategy for winning the presidential nomination is to identify himself with youth. In preparing his first nationwide TV speech, he added Dwight D. Straightarrow, a recent Harvard graduate, to his speechwriting staff. It was his first political blunder. How was he to know that young Straightarrow was the only student to graduate from Harvard since 1960 with a decent education?

"Your job," he said to Straightarrow, "is to give my speeches a youthful flavor. Stick in some sparkling youthful expressions like 'industrial ecological criminals,' 'militaristic mass murderers,' 'Southern racial bigots,' and 'Middle-American anti–intellectuals.' "

Young Straightarrow began reading the speech and immediately said, *"Wow!"*

"That's a youthful expression, all right!" cried the Senator. "Should I stick it in the beginning?"

"It's this beginning you'd better stick, sir," said his young employee. "Where you say, 'The American Dream has become a nightmare to American youth.' Where did you get that?"

"It's a rewrite of the exact same thing Senator Kennedy said in Massachusetts."

"Senator Kennedy can say *any*thing in Massachusetts," chuckled young Straightarrow, recalling some of the things Senator Kennedy had said when he was a student there. "But no one else can get away with it anywhere else. According to the latest Gallup poll, when youth on 200 campuses were asked if they still considered America the land of opportunity, 87 percent said yes."

"I hope they don't find that out in Massachusetts," said Chuck, who, although a rival for the presidential candidacy, was a friend of Ted's. "Anything else bother you?"

"This part about how hopeless and bitter America's young blacks are because they have no future in racist white America. That's a laugh."

"It's a rewrite of something Senator Ribicoff said," the Senator bridled, "and nobody laughed at *him.*"

"Whom did he say it to?"

"The ADA."

"Lucky for him he didn't try it on a bunch that knew something. Or they'd have known that the same Gallup poll found that while 72 percent of all whites were optimistic about their future in America, 75 percent of all nonwhites are. And that the average income of the young black married couple has now reached 7 percent higher than that of young whites."

"Throw the line away," sighed the Senator.

"I'll save it," said young Straightarrow, "for your Yale speech. Kingman Brewster will give you an honorary degree."

"I hope you're not going to mess up my ecology stuff," grumbled the Senator, "about how the military-industrial complex is committing legal murder by making our air unfit to breathe. It's a rewrite of something I heard Ralph Nader himself say on the Johnny Carson show. The audience applauded wildly."

"The Carson audience *always* applauds wildly when they hold up a 'WILD APPLAUSE' card," his young assistant explained patiently. "But people who know something will be listening to *you,* and they'll hit you with this report from the National Science Foundation as published in the *New York Times:* 'Seventy-eight samples of air were recently collected at different sites around the world and were compared with air samples taken 60 years ago. There is precisely the same amount of oxygen in the air today as there was in 1910.' "

"That blows my whole speech," snarled the Senator. "Why don't my writers know enough *not* to give me things that are untrue."

"Maybe," said young Straightarrow, "they know that anything you say to a liberal audience, as long as it discredits America, will get 'em standing up and cheering!"

"It will?" asked the Senator with a sudden twinkle in his eye.

"Yep," said the young Straightarrow, sadly.

The Senator fired young Straightarrow and gave the speech without any changes. Although a few soreheads, including the National Science Foundation, the Gallup poll, 54% of the public, and Spiro Agnew, grumbled, he was hailed by Justice William O. Douglas, Arthur Schlesinger, Jr., and Gloria Steinem as "a youthful voice of honest despair at the refusal of America to face the truth about its problems."

SLOBBIDGE IS MY NAME

When P. U. Slobbidge, whose truck, emblazoned "Slobbidge is my Name and Garbage is my Game," is one of the glories of Spillover, New Jersey, read that his government had just provided $40 million in seed capital to encourage new small business ventures, he hoped that his dream of a two-truck empire might, at last, come true.

One truck had been enough for the community, until 746 welfare families were moved into the new $30 million public housing project, and 746 nonwelfare families, and their surviving unmugged old folks and children, moved out.

Their modest homes were immediately razed and the neighborhood transformed into a golf course for the residents of the public housing project.

However, while the number of people living in Spillover remained the same, the amount of garbage doubled, and the quality, Slobbidge noted, was better. Better cuts of meat, better brands of canned foods, and wine bottles from better years.

"Those food stamps," he smiled, "certainly bring me into contact with a better class of leavings."

He was ushered into the office of Laidley Godiva, the fund commissioner.

"I hope I'm not too late to get a piece of that $40 million . . ."

96

"You're the first applicant," beamed the commissioner. "The entire $40 million is right here"—he tapped his big green voucher book with his pen—"straining to be released by my signature on these vouchers, to help the humble and worthy."

"Slobbidge," began the applicant, "is my name, and garbage is my game."

"You'll never believe this," gasped the commissioner, "but, although I've served in every field of government, you, sir, are my first contact with—er—your field. To me there's always been a mysterious air about it. An air, I assure you, sir, I am about to dispel!"

He summoned his $275 a week secretary, and worth every cent of it.

"I must know more about garbage . . ." he began.

"What's to know?" interjected the applicant. "I've been in it all my life. Up to here. It just a lot o' . . ."

The commissioner wagged a gently restraining figure, and issued the following instructions to his secretary. "Appoint a $14 million study group to get to the bottom of garbage." He quickly made out a voucher for that sum, and handed it to her. "Get me the unadulterated facts. Like where it comes from . . ."

"I can NAME the slobs!" cried Slobbidge heatedly.

The commissioner beckoned him to resume his seat, and gave him a cigar.

"Try to get the President of Yale, or Abbie Hoffman's publisher, as Chairman. Someone who is familiar with garbage."

The secretary left. "And now to your community's problem, Mr. Slobbidge."

"It's the same as lots of communities where there's public housing. The problem is there's twice as much to haul as there are trucks for hauling."

"That gives me an idea!" exclaimed the comissioner, opening the voucher book again, taking his pen in one hand, and pushing a buzzer with the other.

"$900 is all I need for a down payment on another truck," began Mr. Slobbidge, but the commissioner didn't hear him. Another $275-a-week secretary had entered who, clearly, could have earned twice as much in Las Vegas.

"I want a $22 million study group appointed," the commisioner said, handing her a voucher for the sum, "to find out why, although they say there's more starvation in America than ever before, there's also more garbage. Especially in places where they're supposed to be starving." She left and the commissioner began filling out another voucher.

"Could you make that one for $900?" asked Mr. Slobbidge, who had done some fast mental arithmetic and realized that the way things were going, he'd better get his fast. "It's all I need for a second-hand truck . . ."

"First things first," said the commissioner. He summoned another secretary who, although seemingly content with her $275 a week, would have been sick at the thought that crossed Mr. Slobbidge's mind, namely, that it would be worth paying her twice as much, to Raquel Welch's producers, to keep her out of movies.

"I want you," the commissioner instructed her, "to create a study group to come up with a pilot project for America's first totally garbage-free community. One where all religions and income levels are represented and live in harmony. Try to get Pete Seeger or Ralph Nader as chairman." He handed her the voucher.

"H-how much was that for?" asked Mr. Slobbidge.

"As a taxpayer," replied the commissioner, "you're entitled to know. $4 million. And now, sir, what can I do for you?"

"Skip it," said Mr. Slobbidge, leaving. He had done another bit of fast mental arithmetic. The $40 million had been spent on commissions to study the garbage problem. There wasn't a dime left to remove it.

THE PLAN OF THE APES

The Senate cave was filling, and the first low grunts of greeting built into an ear-splitting cacaphony of shrieks, bellows, and breast-pounding as the elected representatives of the people gathered.

As usual, a few representatives of nonpeople (a dinosaur, a

three-toed sloth, and a blue-nosed baboon) tried to get in, but they were clubbed out and told to come back when they'd evolved, and not one millennium before.

The president of the Senate called for the chaplain to dance the daily prayer, and the great lawmaking body was in session.

The debate was begun by revered old Sen. J. Willugg Fullcrok, the first man to develop human speech from grunting to chronic whining.

"Fellow subhumans," he whined, "this proposed new weapons system simply will not work. It's a waste of taxpayers' money and I want the statement to go into the record."

The Senate clerk picked up a flat rock and a flint chisel and began his 28-year job of putting the statement into the record.

Tree-dwelling Birch Biter, the Senate's only bark-eating member, arose;

"I concur with the Father of American Whining. The new weapons system is an unproven thing. I vote not to get involved with such an unpredictable and unnecessarily expensive element as *fire!*"

That word inflamed a peace demonstration by a pack of half-grown chimpanzees outside. They began leaping up and down, making obscene gestures, and shrieking their slogan: "Make glug— not fire!"

As their frenzy mounted, a few of the furrier ones began lobbing rocks at the lawmakers, but then Sen. Teddugg, the youth idol, rose and spoke.

"Let's spend our money on things we need!" he cried. "Like training more witch doctors for the National Health Service. There are children who still go to bed at night suffering from the spell cast by the Uncooked Vegetable Devil! They could have been saved if there was a witch doctor around to do a simple devil-chasing wonggo dance. Instead of putting our money into such crazy experiments as fire," he cried, "let's put it into education—like extra courses in lamentations and incantations for witch doctors!"

Teddugg sat down to thunderous applause from the chimpanzees outside.

Unfortunately, they had no votes, and the older, wiser, pointed heads in the Senate voted the appropriation. And that is why, today, man enjoys fire and all its blessings, such as ceramic ashtrays and Col. Sanders Kentucky Fried Chicken.

Aren't you glad we don't live in such a short-sighted society?

Or, do we?

On August 11, 1970, Sen. J. William Fulbright said, "Safeguard simply will *not* work."

On August 19, Sen. Ted Kennedy said, "I have argued time and again that the Safeguard (ABM) system is technically unworkable." On both occasions, Sen. Birch Bayh concurred. Yet on August 31, the Army announced that it had successfully intercepted a missile for the first time with its Safeguard antiballistic missile system (ABM).

MY HONOR, YOUR MAYOR

A chap in the Lindsay administration, who was appointed to a $72,000-a-year job as a youth counsellor while out on $100 bail on 43 charges of purse-snatching in Central Park, sent me a copy of the following letter. He claims it will be mailed to all New York City voters, three years from now, when Mayor Lindsay is up for reelection.

Dear Voter:

As Election Day 1975 approaches, remember the major accomplishment of my administration: I have totally eliminated air pollution.

Your slim, stalwart, superbly barbered mayor didn't accomplish this in a flash of genius. Frankly, dear friend and voter, I made the same mistakes any blundering incompetent might make. The difference was, I didn't give up. I went on making them.

But then I got the hang of it. I began by barring private automobiles from certain streets in New York City during certain times of the day. That lowered air pollution levels on those streets for those days, and so I went onto the next step.

I barred *all* private automobiles from New York City forever.

This, of course, had the effect of forcing eight million people to use a subway and bus system that hadn't been able to handle three million. There was some grumbling, I'm told, but I couldn't hear it in my limousine gliding swiftly through New York City streets, uncongested and quiet for the first time in history. And for the first time, my Honor, your Mayor, could make it to city hall in 15 minutes instead of the usual hour and a half, giving me 9 extra hours per week to work for your good.

Even with all private automobiles but mine barred from our city's streets, air pollution had not been completely eliminated, and so, knowing that I might be criticized for it, I took the next sensible step: I barred all vehicles: trucks, police cars, fire engines, ambulances.

My political enemies complained that people were dying every day because there were no ambulances to take them to our city hospitals, but I quickly replied that even before the ban, people had died every day, even after we *got* them to our city hospitals, and that many of them were *glad* to when they realized where they were.

Still, the carbon monoxide was a fraction too high. Trifling as this was, it bothered me. Your clean-living, firm-jawed, clear-eyed Mayor is a perfectionist, I guess.

And then the final solution came to me. Not to me personally, I must confess. Give credit where credit is due is what your highly motivated, highly principled Mayor says. It came from a 19-year-old adviser, one of 453 such youths employed on my staff at $35,000 a year, each.

"Carbon monoxide is caused by people, breathing in oxygen," he snarled. "Any fool knows that!"

I said I knew it.

"So ban all people from New York City!" he rasped.

Everybody laughed, except me.

In my quiet, subdued way I saw the possibilities. The next day I banned all people from New York City.

To prove that it wasn't just a move to grab votes, I plugged up all the loopholes. Liberals were banned as well as conservatives. Students as well as hard-hats. I barred the City Council, the Board of Education, Mr. and Mrs. Leonard Bernstein, Harriet Van Horne and Johnny Carson. I even fired my personal chauffeur, and now I drive my own car.

I promised you I'd make New York City a place a man can happily live in, and I am that man.

Sincerely,

John V. Lindsay

WHEN YOU DINE WITH A GABOR—
YOU PAY ATTENTION TO A GABOR

The dread Berrigan Brothers Mob (a couple of jailed Jesuits backed by several ex-nuns, trained in Gregorian chant and hand-to-hand combat), who go under the name of the East Coast Conspiracy, have denied J. Edgar Hoover's charge that they'd plotted to kidnap Prof. Henry Kissinger, the presidential adviser.

It is well known, however, in the ecclesiastical underground, that a previous attempt on the professor by the *West* Coast Conspiracy came within a hair of succeeding. A blonde hair.

That mob, too, was led by a couple of brothers in orders and their sistren. They were all members of a mail-order order, whose ads are familiar to readers of sex and nudie magazines. To qualify for being ordained in the order one must go through a period of study long enough to understand that one must send in $12.50 in cash or money order to a post office box in Berkeley, California, for the documents that entitle you to legally call yourself a Reverend. For the sistren, there is a Limited Special Amazing Offer of an Angel of Mercy's habit, with a concealed hand-grenade pouch, for $67.50, C.O.D.

The West Coast Conspiracy, too, was dedicated to bringing world peace by kidnapping Professor Kissinger, who was destroying world peace by encouraging the President to be discourteous to Communists.

The reverend brothers traveled to Hanoi to seek advice from a fellow religious leader attached to the Temple of Dy Yanki Dy, an ancient Asiatic form of worship, founded a couple of weeks ago by an atheist in the Opium of the Masses Department of the Kremlin.

They found their saintly almond-eyed colleague, Ku Ku Birh Dee (also known as Colonel Bluhd Baath of the North Vietnamese Snipers), removing the hands of a 93-year-old village leader for having made an insolent gesture to a 17-year-old V.C.

"I have a plan," he said, "but it can only be accomplished if you can somehow lure Professor Kissinger into a gay Washington restaurant with Zsa Zsa Gabor."

"Nothing is impossible," replied his American brethren, offering some POWs' letters from their wives in exchange for signed confessions that they regretted committing the war atrocity of keeping a Communist missile site under surveillance.

"The plan is this: Before Miss Gabor and the Professor get past the aperitif, a busboy slips him a note saying, *'Don't act nervous! There is a bomb concealed in the floral centerpiece on your table. It is powerful enough to blow up the joint and all the innocent people in it, including Miss Gabor.*

" 'Don't try to reach for it, because it can be instantly detonated by a remote control device, which is in the possession of someone in this restaurant who is watching you.

" 'You can save your life, and Miss Gabor's, and everyone else's, if you rise now! Inform Miss Gabor that you simply must freshen up, leave the building, and enter the black limousine with the inscrutable almond-eyed driver waiting outside.

" 'Don't try to stall! Our finger is on the detonator, so get cracking and, above all, don't reveal any anxiety about sticking Miss Gabor with the check. Remember, she has dated actors.' "

The plot would have succeeded if only the plotters had had proper information on a key factor: Miss Gabor's temperament.

When the busboy slipped the Professor the note, she snatched it out of his hands before he could read it and ripped it to shreds screaming, "Ven you're out mit a Gabor, from udder girls you dunt get notes!"

4-year-olds are barred from seeing Elliott Gould in the nude,
a privilege millions of other Americans enjoy.

THE DAY THE KIDS WOULDN'T SWALLOW SILVERSPOON

Sen. Sonny Silverspoon who nosed out Mick Jagger in both the Gallup and Downbeat polls as Youth Idol of the Year, had a long-range plan to win the presidential nomination of both parties in 1984, which would have made him the first 59-year-old Youth Idol President in history.

The plan was worked out by his "Inner Circle" (CBS, NBC, ABC, the faculty of Harvard, and the editorial staffs of 237 Eastern newspapers) at a secret meeting at his family compound (the entire East Coast).

They were summoned there hastily after the stunning setback to the Senator's presidential aspirations last summer when he won the fight to reduce the voting age from 18 to 15. But that was just a few tragic hours before the figures were released showing that the average 15-year-old was too smart to vote for him, and that the average 12-year-old was, too, and that the only bunch who would were 4-year-olds (except for voters of *all* ages in the Senator's home state).

The Senator's Inner Circle advised him to immediately launch his campaign against chronological discrimination: namely, depriving people of equal voting rights just because they happened to be born a few years ago, namely 4.

He called a press conference in the toy store his family had just bought for him, and entered wearing a pink bunny costume, playing a Popeye guitar, and snapping bubble gum. With a bang of his rattle, he stated (in language his Inner Circle told him would identify him with youth); "Any nassy old member of the Pwess who doesn't stop pwaying with *my* erector set just better leave my party and go homey-bye!"

With order restored, he continued; "Goodness gumdwops! No

boy or girl can help being *four*! Nobody ever asked them if they wanted to be. Nobody ever asked them if they wanted to be *one*!"

He stamped his foot until the bells on his toes jingled.

"Our four-year-olds never WANTED to come here. They were forced. Some by forceps!

"And how do we tweet them? Nassy and mean! They're barred from seeing movies with Elliott Gould in the nude, a privilege any other American can enjoy any night of the week!"

"They can go to Walt Disney movies," snarled a hostile reporter from *Tiny Tots* magazine.

"Where they are forced to sit in *front*!" retorted the Senator. "But—can a four-year-old get a job in any of the new, high-paying, fast-growing professions, such as *bomb-demolition at Harvard?*

"Or can one be a fireman? Every four-year-old is just dying to be a fireman, but nobody ever lets them be one!!! They don't even get to ride on a fire twuck.

"And you talk about sexism," he said, sticking his tongue out at a Women's Lib columnist from *Polly Pigtails*. "Statistics pwoove that at least half of all four-year-olds are girls! But do they ever get a chance to burn their bwas? Nobody ever BUYS them bwas!"

His long pink ears trembled with indignation.

"Spiro Agnew cwiticizes us for having tantrums. To pawaphwase Hubert Humphrey—'If I were a four-year-old I might have a pwetty good tantrum myself!' "

At these words, the cold, cynical members of the press broke down. Some openly wept.

His campaign against chronological discrimination had gotten off to a blazing start that might, in time, have carried him to the White House. But tragedy stalked again.

That very night the figures were released by the President's Commission To Study the Projected Intelligence of the Four-Year-Old of the Future. They showed that at the present rate of intellectual growth, the average four-year-old would be too smart to vote for Senator Silverspoon by the time they got the vote.

His Inner Circle held another emergency meeting. They advised him to abandon his campaign against chronological discrimination, because it wouldn't do the nation as much good as they thought.

SIMPLE PLEASURES OF THE HUMBLE

Life becomes more complicated every day, but there are still simple pleasures we can all enjoy, such as not seeing an Elliott Gould movie. It costs nothing, yet those who have tried it, rave about it. You look through the movie ads, select the nearest theater at which an Elliott Gould movie is playing, stay home instead, and, at the instant the movie comes on, start staring at a blank wall.

It may sound dull, but those who have tried it say the simple pleasure of not seeing Elliott Gould, in the nude, in living color, on a wide screen, will make you understand why it was a privilege Barbra Streisand was willing to give up.

Then there is the simple pleasure of not taking a walk at night in New York City, which gives you the same pleasurable sensation as not getting mugged. The only greater pleasure, they say, is not living in New York at all, and waking up anyplace else in the world and realizing that John Lindsay isn't your mayor.

Then there is the simple pleasure of taking time off from listening to Ralph Nader's complaints about the imperfections of the products of American industry, to enjoy their near-perfection. And to take some comfort knowing that although they aren't good enough yet for Ralph Nader, or for American industry itself, either, they are still better than the products of any other industry, anywhere else in the world.

A simple pleasure more and more of us are taking advantage of every day is not listening to David Susskind. It is a pleasure the humblest of us can enjoy, except, of course, those who are hooked on words like "dichotomy," "simplistic" and "Judaeo-Christian ethic." Only place you can still get that stuff is on David Susskind programs, but even then, you can get it all in any five-minute dose of David, which is as harmless as hemlock.

Then there's the simple pleasure of *not* feeling compelled to look young. It takes time to get into shape for that, but it's worth every decade.

Take John Mitchell and Charles Goodell, for example. They're both middle-aged, they both have about the same amount of hair.

John Mitchell doesn't feel compelled to look young or be young. He's frankly bald. He looks comfortably middle-aged; he talks comfortable middle-aged talk. He's working steady.

Charles Goodell combs his hair up from his armpits, uses words like "rap," "relate" and "dig," wears wide ties and long sideburns, clearly convinced that if he didn't look young, he'd be out of style. Instead he's out of work.

Avoiding Jane Fonda is a simple pleasure any American can enjoy, except a few American Indians. Not reading *The Greening of America* is a pleasant way to spend an evening at home, enjoying not being infuriated by the author's theory that if you are old enough to support a home you are the intellectual inferior of any sullen pubescent in it who freeloads on you.

And then there is the simplest pleasure of all; the pleasure of admitting to yourself that although you may not have voted for Richard Nixon (as I didn't), your fellow Americans chose a cool and competent President. It's a pleasure lots of us would rather die than try, but those of us who have, feel a lot better about things than we did.

SIMPLE PLEASURES OF THE CELEBRATED

After I wrote a column on the simple pleasures of humble people, a lot of celebrated people wrote in and told me they enjoyed simple pleasures, too. Frankly, I doubt the authenticity of some of these letters, especially this one which was signed "Dick C." who claims he runs a TV talk show:

"Dear Al:

"Although anyone who has ever watched my TV show for any three-minute period realizes that I went to Yale and am agonizingly superior to the dolts I am forced to interview, I sometimes get a simple pleasure out of it. Especially when I invite some simple Southern Governor on, and confront him with a couple of New York buddies of mine who call him a racist. And when he tells us the simple truth that, in the last election, 75 percent of the blacks in his state voted for him, my buddies and I all ignore that. We continue to abuse him. He walks off the show. We continue to abuse him.

"It's a simple pleasure any TV talk show host can enjoy because Southerners are so simple they believe that any one who went to Yale must be a gentleman and that gentlemen don't humiliate their guests."

This one was signed "J. William F." who wants me to believe he is not only a U.S. Senator, but a member of the Foreign Relations Committee:

"Dear Al:

"I have only one pleasure left, and it is a mighty simple one. I complain about anything any American does to any Communist; but have you ever heard of any Communist who ever complained about me?"

The next one was signed "John L." who says he's mayor of some city where several people will not be mugged tonight, because they're out of town:

"Dear Al:

"I'll bet mine is the simplest pleasure of all. I won't commit myself one way or another, and so the Republicans are afraid I won't switch, and the Democrats are afraid I will."

This one was signed "Ted," who says that one of his hobbies is avoiding symphony concerts.

"Dear Al:

"I'm enjoying the simple pleasure of trying to limit the amount of money a candidate can spend in a campaign. I got the idea by imagining Raquel Welch trying to limit the amount of bosom Phyllis Diller could show in a movie."

"Ed M." who says he's well-known in Maine wrote:

"Dear Al:

"A few weeks ago I enjoyed the simple pleasure of stopping the development of the SST on the grounds that it might be a threat to the environment. I wish I'd been around 75 years ago, when we were developing the automobile. I could have stopped that, on the grounds that it would be a threat to the environment, and kept us all on horses, although I seem to recall that they were occasionally threats to the environment."

The simplest letter was from a fella named "Carl F——n" who is the ex-husband of a Women's Liberation leader "Betty F——n" and who said his greatest pleasure was being that.

HOW TO SOLVE CRIME IN THE STREETS

It will be easy to solve the problem of crime in the streets as soon as we realize that all the data in all studies on the subject are right —but that the conclusions we draw from them are wrong. According to the studies, the average mugger is an unemployed younger man. His victim is an employed older man. So far—so good.

Let's look at a typical case.

A young man named Tom sees an older man named Jerry on the street in the evening. Tom is bursting with energy. Tom is on welfare. But forgive me for repeating myself.

Tom has slept till 3 P.M. There was no point getting up any earlier because his welfare check won't arrive until tomorrow. Tomorrow Tom will get up early to prevent his neighbor, Joe, who is also on welfare, from prying open his mailbox and stealing his check.

Tom ate a hearty breakfast, watched cartoons on TV for a couple of hours, dropped in on the unwed mother next door to pass the time of day, and is now out for his evening stroll. He is at peace with the world, although he hasn't a dollar in his pocket and is careful not to stroll any place he can earn one.

Along comes Jerry. He is not as energetic as Tom. He arose at dawn to get to his job. He worked a full eight hours, put in two hours overtime, and is now going to the corner to buy the evening paper.

At the sight of Jerry, Tom's peace is shattered. A sense of injustice burns in his bosom. There is a bulge in Jerry's coat. It is the bulge of a wallet. Tom remembers that he was taught at school that the American Dream is that all men are created equal. So Tom mugs Jerry and runs off with his wallet. The creates an equal bulge in Tom's pocket.

He has made the American dream come true. Our studies have revealed that there are thousands of such incidents in our streets every night, and society could prevent them all by making one simple, obvious move no study has yet had the simple common sense to point out.

The instant Jerry—or anyone like him who earns his living— gets home on payday, society must take his money—*all* of it—away from him and give it to Tom.

Then and *only* then will there be no more crime in the streets. Not having the money to go out and get the evening paper will keep Jerry safely at home and spare Tom the necessity of mugging him, which is not only illegal, but looks bad on Tom's record when he is offered a $12,000-a-year job on the community improvement commission he has been saving himself for.

We will stop crime in the streets only when we face the fact all the studies make so crystal clear. It isn't the muggers who are to blame, but stubborn *us,* who won't give up our wallets *until* we're mugged.

THE PSYCHOS FROM NEBRASKA

There was an hour's delay in all traffic at National Airport in Washington last week. I noted one empty seat at a table in the cafeteria and I was warmly invited to share it by a family from Hastings, Nebraska, Mr. and Mrs. W. C. Overflow and their teenage son, Harvey.

"We can't wait to get home," said Mr. Overflow. "Not that we haven't had an amazing week in Washington. What happened to us was so fantastic that we can't wait to tell folks about it."

"They'll never believe us," said Mrs. Overflow. "It's too fantastic."

"I doubt if any three people who ever came to Washington had the fantastic things happen to them we've had," said young Harvey, "including John Wilkes Booth, Bobby Baker, and Harry Truman."

"It's not very nice to arouse this poor man's curiosity and leave him dangling," said Mrs. Overflow. "You," she said to her husband, "owe it to him to tell him what happened to *you*."

"I will," said Mr. Overflow, "but don't feel you owe it to me to listen to it all. Any time it gets too fantastic stop me. Well, one night the wife was worn out from sightseeing and young Harvey here wanted to catch a TV show, so I decided to take a little stroll and see the Capitol by moonlight."

"If I'd had the slightest idea I'd have stopped him. By force, if necessary," said Mrs. Overflow.

"I never knew Dad had a crazy streak in him!" said young Harvey, admiringly.

Overflow chuckled. "Well, sir," he said, "I strolled to the Capitol. I stopped and looked at it by moonlight. Then I strolled back. That's my story."

"Not the *whole* story," I said.

"The whole story," said Mr. Overflow, firmly.

"I told you he wouldn't believe it" said his wife.

"I do," I assured her. "As far as it went. But he's left something out."

"Like what?" asked Mr. Overflow.

"The mugging," I said.

"I wasn't mugged," he said.

I arose.

"If you people asked me to share your table to make a fool of me . . ."

"Sit down," said Mrs. Overflow. "If you think *his* story is fantastic, listen to mine. The afternoon the Smithsonian was on our schedule, I told the boys to go ahead and I'd join them later. I wanted to do some shopping. It was a lovely afternoon, so instead of taking a cab, I walked through the park to the Smithsonian and joined them."

"Madam!" I said, rising again. "If you begin a story please have the decency to *finish* it!"

The lady who walked through a park in Washington, D.C. and wasn't raped.

"I did finish it," she said.

I snorted. "Suppose I were an unaccompanied female. Suppose I told you I took a walk through a park in Washington, D.C., unarmed and unescorted. And *then* suppose I told you I'd reached my destination, would *you* believe it? Or would you know darn well I'd left something out?"

"Like what?" asked Mrs. Overflow.

"Like the . . . well . . . I hate to mention it, but . . . what about the rape?"

"I *wasn't* raped," said Mrs. Overflow.

I rose again.

"I've never been to Hastings, Nebraska," I said, "but I'll bet folks there are just as smart as they are anyplace else. You go back and tell them stories like *that* about their nation's capital and they'll send out the boys with the butterfly nets!"

Young Harvey grabbed my arm and forced me back to my seat.

"Suppose I told you that I looked out of my hotel window one evening and saw a man park a Cadillac in front of an office building across the street. And suppose I told you that although several teen-agers were loitering on that street, when that man came out of that building, fifteen minutes later, the car was still there!"

I wrenched myself out of his grasp, dashed out of the cafeteria and called the psychiatric ward of the Walter Reed Hospital. I told them to rush to the airport and apprehend three babbling, and possibly dangerous, lunatics. When they arrived, I tried to repeat the stories they'd told me, but I'm afraid I wasn't as maniacally calm about it as they were.

When I told the one about Mr. Overflow taking a walk in Washington at night and not being mugged, it sounded like babble, even to me. And when I got to the part about the lady not being raped, I'm afraid I fell to the floor in a fit of mocking laughter. But it wasn't until I came to where the Cadillac wasn't stolen that one of the men in the white coats said, "Take *him* away."

SUFFER LITTLE CHILDREN TO THROW MOLOTOV COCKTAILS

When I heard that the police of East Providence, R. I., were being given special classes in the three Cs (How to Keep Their Cool, Cheerfulness, and Composure While Being Subjected to Student Villification, Expectoration, and Mutilation), I dropped by.

A three Cs instructor was addressing a class of rookies.

"We learned the value of keeping our Cool, Cheerfulness, and Composure from our mistakes in Chicago," he was saying. "Take the case of Patrolman Polanski, 48, 27 years on the force, father of seven parochial school graduates and one seminarian. When he was surrounded by a mob of peace protestors, hurling paving blocks, broken bottles, and cherry bombs at him, and yelling, 'Kill the pig!' what do you think Polanski did?"

"Tell us what Polanski did to them little creeps!" cried the rookies, thirsting for guidance.

"He made the same mistake *you* just did," replied the instructor severely. "He overreacted. *He* called them little creeps, too! Result: a suit slapped on him by the American Civil Liberties Union for defaming their characters, causing them grievous humilation, and depriving them of their freedom to dissent. Any questions?"

"What should Polanski have done to them little ladies and gentlemen?" asked the rookies.

"If he had mastered his three Cs, he'd have kept his cool, cheerfulness, and composure until their attention span, which is very short, had run out. They'd have found something else to do—a squad car to tip over or a bank to burn—and they'd have gone harmlessly on their way.

"Patrolman Polanski could then have picked up his teeth, and been commended for his understanding of youth's hopes and dreams, instead of being suspended on charges.

"Or take the case of Lt. LeRoi Abernathy of the Washington,

"Tell us what Polanski did to them little creeps."

D.C., force," the instructor continued, "a father of nine, including two marines, and himself a part-time preacher. In a recent demonstration protesting the brutality of police to minority groups, the back of the lieutenant's skull was split by a broken Coke bottle hurled by Abbie Hoffwit, the youth leader. Although Hoffwit attempted to conceal himself by blowing his nose into an American flag, the lieutenant apprehended him.

"To get him into the paddy wagon, it was necessary to whack him in the butt with a nightstick. It was this scene, and this scene alone, that the TV cameras recorded. Since it was in black and white, the blood flowing down the lieutenant's neck photographed as dark as his skin and was indistinguishable. The picture made the front page of a liberal Washington newspaper, and the lieutenant was demoted for leading a 'police riot!'

"All because," sighed the instructor, "he wasn't instructed in the three Cs—Coolness, Cheerfulness, and Composure when facing students. Any questions?"

Rookie Alex N. Wonderland raised his hand.

"Why can't students be taught the three Cs when facing us?" he asked. "Not to Curse us, not to Crunch our skulls, and not to Call us pigs because of our color, which is blue?"

Rookie Wonderland was instantly dismissed from the class and assigned to desk duty, where he will spend the rest of his life because he does not understand the hopes and dreams of restless youth.

THERE'S A LITTLE BULZCHT IN EVERY CULTURE CENTER

I was certainly surprised to find that the headquarters of Boris Bulzcht, director of the Washington, D.C., Festival of Art, Drama, and Music, was located in Hastings, Nebraska.

"Is this location as handy as Washington?"

"Not for the muggers in Washington," he chuckled.

I made a note that Bulzcht wasn't all aesthete, but had a strong streak of the practical.

"Your festival has had a sensational opening season," I said. "Every one of your plays, concerts, ballets, and art exhibitions has received rave reviews from the Washington critics, the news magazines, and the world press. To what do you attribute this triumph?"

"To the United States Congress," replied Bulzcht, reverently. "Both houses."

I expressed my astonishment that a sensitive artist should pay tribute to a bunch of politicians.

"They came through for Bulzcht when Bulzcht needed them," he replied, "which was last year when I asked for an additional $180,000,000 in petty cash to put the finishing touches on our $14 billion Festival Center building.

"Frankly, I could have used more than that, but with all the poverty around, I decided to do my bit by canceling Picasso's contract to do the murals in the powder rooms, and turned a bunch of 7-year-old kids loose in them, with buckets of tar and brushes, and achieved the same effect.

"I made my request for merely $180 million because I had been tipped off that that was *all* the money the government had *left*.

"There must have been a leak, though, because at the very same time, the Washington Police Department made a request for exactly the same amount, to double the force and stop the muggings and murders.

"A few heartless and inhuman Congressmen voted to spend the money to lower the murder and mugging rate, but they were beaten by the more idealistic ones who explained that putting more money into putting more cops on the street was merely dealing with the *symptoms* of crime, and not the causes, which were insufficient Benjamin Britten operas, Berthold Brecht plays, and Andy Warhol exhibitions.

"Well, when the Washington police realized that although the numbers of criminals roaming the streets would continue to rise, the number of cops would remain the same, half of them resigned. And when the remaining half realized that *they* now had only *half* as much chance of staying alive, they resigned, too.

Every culture center needs a little Bulzcht.

"They didn't want to be the only nonmuggers and nonmurderers out after dark.

"The night after the Washington police gave up, the festival opened with an opera.

"None of the performers dared to leave their hotel rooms.

"But none of the ticket holders complained. They didn't know: they didn't dare to leave their homes.

"The critics, of course, were the most chicken of all. They locked themselves in their homes in the suburbs, and phoned in their reviews.

"Because of their guilt feelings, the reviews were raves.

"The season was off to a triumphant start. And it went on that way to a triumphant finale.

"Because there was no police protection, there were no performers, no audiences, no critics—nothing but rave reviews.

"*Time* and *Newsweek* sent correspondents from New York. When they heard there was no police protection in Washington, they got off at Baltimore, picked up the Washington papers, and rewrote their rave reviews into raves of their own.

"The international press picked up their raves, and translated them.

"My festival," smiled Bulzcht, "became the talk and envy of the world. I have received offers to stage festivals in Paris, London, and Rome."

"But is there enough Bulzcht to go around?" I asked.

"*I'm* staying here," he replied firmly. "Let them get Bulzcht artists of their own. Only America will vote millions to provide a culture center for the public, but not a dime to provide police enough to make it possible for the public to leave their homes at night and enjoy it."

120

ST. MARY'S COLLEGE OF MARYLAND
ST. MARY'S CITY, MARYLAND

054358